Janet V. ....

The Angel Within

Foreword by The Lord Rix Kt CBE DL

Williams Publications

First Published in 1994 by The Publishing Corporation U.K. Ltd.

Published in 2004 by Williams Publications.

A CIP catalogue record for this book is available from the British Library.

ISBN   0-9548598-0-4

NB Helen Wade is a pseudonym of Janet Wade.

Printed in England by: Intype Libra,Wimbledon. SW19 4HE

Marketing and Sales:
Williams Publications
8 Ranulph Way
Hatfield Peverel
Essex CM3 2RN
Tel: 01245 381064

By the same author:

Safe as Houses (to be published in 2005)

For Neil and Jonathan

Acknowledgement

I am greatly indebted to:-
The Lord Rix Kt CBE DL, who has written the foreword,
Mr. Graham Petley for allowing the use of an original painting
for the cover, and a special daughter without whom this book
would have had no cause to be written.

Foreword
By
The Lord Rix Kt CBE DL

The story begins in Canada 40 years ago, and that context and timing are important in reading the early pages of this fascinating and eminently reasonable book.

Fresh from sharing with her husband her handicapped daughter's first word, Helen Wade found herself saying of that daughter, "She'll be debating in the Upper Chamber before your first grey hair." (The Upper House in question was the Canadian Senate, not the Westminster House of Lords.) Daughter 'Minty' seems to have harboured no aspirations for membership of Parliament either side of the Atlantic; and husband Bob died a comparatively young man, presumably without many grey hairs.

However, for all that catalogue of unfulfilled dreams, I can't help thinking that some future UK Government, unsure what to do about our Second Chamber, could do worse than include in a reformed 'Senate' of the relevantly great and good some people with learning disability like the 'Minties' of this world. There are people with learning disability who might have so much more to offer than some of the officials and experts whose insensitivity and incompetence spice the pages of the Wade family story.

Among the virtues that those of us who sit in the present House of Lords are supposed to display - sometimes in contrast to "the Other Place" - are commonsense, willingness to listen, tolerance of different views and all manner of people, an instinct for justice, and a readiness to see the best in the worst. There are people with learning disabilities who fit that job description admirably; and most of those who do are not prone to make long-winded speeches full of jargon!

The 'Minty' story begins some decades ago when the language around learning disability was less sensitive, the knowledge of the social/educational/health care aspects of learning disability generally much poorer, and the attitudes towards people with learning disability far less positive. I, and others of the older generation of parents, recognise the experiences of those early years all too well. Parents of younger children and those coming fresh to disability need to remember that things have changed. What has not changed is the very individual nature of being a parent with a disabled child. Nor is there any change in the important reality that every person with a learning disability is different from every other person with a learning disability - whatever may be said about syndromes and phenotypes and about 'them' all being alike.

This is the sometimes funny, sometimes deeply moving, story of the ups and downs of one family, with its own strengths and weaknesses. It is also the story of others who helped or hindered. The hindering often came from indifference, from wearing Doc Martins where dancing shoes were needed, or from glib pronouncements based on ignorance masquerading as expertise. The helping often came from simply being there, from accepting 'Minty' for herself, and from being honest.

The moral debate about the two sexual issues of sterilisation and marriage is raised by the book rather than followed through; and some readers will respect Helen Wade's insights without agreeing with her conclusions. What gladdened my heart, on the fringes of that debate, is the section which describes Minty's turning to famous men of the theatre and the TV screen for friendship when she found that the hoped for boy friend and future husband never appeared. Those stars found time to respond personally and with real warmth, and the pleasure they gave to a rather lonely and disappointed young woman with Down's syndrome speaks volumes for their insight and compassion. (I hope that compassion hasn't become politically incorrect - it is too valuable a human quality to go out of fashion.)

Read this book. Don't skim it. If you skim you will miss the all-important moments which tell how a family with a disabled daughter missed out on all sorts of things they had expected, and indeed planned, but secured so many joys and satisfactions that were wholly unexpected and wholly unplanned. The name 'Minty' came from an early pleasurable lick at a candy in a doctor's surgery. 'Taste and see' is the message of this book. Those with religious convictions will finish the quotation; those, who claim no such convictions, will still find much that is good to taste in life with a son or daughter with learning disability.

Brian Rix

Author's Preface

Hundreds of biographies are published each year but one in which the central character not only has Downs Syndrome, but makes a unique contribution to the everyday lives of members of her family, seemed a refreshing idea. To hand were diaries kept since our daughter's birth, which would ensure the book would be a far cry from a technical text on 'how to cope', or a sanctimonious guide on methods to be adopted.

It would be an honest reflection of days when we *didn't* cope, as well as those when we did; of occasions when we lacked the courage to be honest either with each other or ourselves. Days in which we could only imagine a bleak future, disbelieving that we would ever cross the bridge from despair to hope, but also of days when we laughed, and our souls sang. And too, it must include an admission that normality sometimes leaned on handicap for an uncluttered approach, and a refusal to be bound by convention.

Most importantly the book must reflect a whole family that *included* a handicapped member as an equal part, but who was not the sole focus; a story of the interdependence of love and trust; of acknowledging the complexity of a situation whilst simultaneously reducing - but not trivialising - that complexity to simple terms.

Her story must lend dignity to both handicap and the human endeavour to absorb it. If, in addressing the whole gamut of emotions involved, it increased awareness and understanding as a result, then it would achieve its aim of being a dedication to those who live with their retardation, and whose courage goes unsung because they are unable to articulate their fears. Their emotions are as acute as in any other individual, and their joy and misery as profound. Without the eloquence to express either, and lacking the intellectual clout to act from a position of strength, they are so often misinterpreted and undervalued.

J.W.

NB: For this reprint edition, and lest some of the text is now considered 'politically incorrect', it must be stated that the book reflects the language surrounding mental disability in the years from 1960. 'Downs syndrome' and 'mental disability' have long replaced the harsher sounding 'mongolism.'

The Angel Within

CHAPTER ONE

The snow was falling heavily again, and settled on our shoulders as we walked. I was still new enough to the Canadian scene to appreciate the crunchy packing beneath our boots as we sank a few inches into the upper layer. I could feel the crisp, icy cold on my lips, and my face glowed in the keenness of the air.

"Remember London slush?" Bob's question had broken the silence, but I knew our thoughts had been in tune.

We turned off Second Street into the little used road leading to the surgery, and came up against a two foot high road block built by enthusiastic youngsters who knew all too well that if 'Doc' had needed to get out to a patient in a hurry, he could just as easily leave by the back of his house. Hedges and fences were not, as in England, an essential part of the landscape, and whilst the lack of them was strange - almost insecure - to the English eye, so there was nothing to inhibit informal, neighbourly access between house and street.

"Hold on to your bonnet Suzie!" Bob had fitted shortened skis beneath the buggy wheels so there was no difficulty in surmounting the obstacle.

Soon we were removing our heavy outdoor coats in response to the welcoming warmth of the waiting room, and the Nurse-Receptionist hung them on the pine room divider. As was both courteous and inevitable, she enquired about the new baby - though she was now three months old. This was our cue to show off, and remark as modestly as we found possible, just how wonderfully good she was, how much weight she had gained, and generally how speedily she was progressing. Which all goes to show how wrong you can be as newcomers to the world of Parenthood, and how dangerously biased.

Doctor Cruickshank's face appeared at the dispensary hatch. "Come on through," he said. And then, as I got up with the baby, leaving Bob behind with a magazine, he added, "No, no...both o'ye. You're the last patients tonight and we can have a chat."

"Don't make it too long," Bob whispered good humouredly, knowing full well that he, and not the Doctor, was the cause of more than one prolonged conversation between the two of them. "I'm hungry."

Doc Cruickshank seemed unusually quiet tonight, his gaze intent as he routinely chest-tapped and weighed, almost 'stagey', as though he had only assumed the role of Doctor for a theatrical production, even to the point of forgetting his lines.

"Doctor..." I began hesitantly. "Is there anything...?" and then feeling awkward, I allowed the question to get lost.

"Is she gud fer ye?" Doc asked the question without raising his eyes. Instinct told me he was stalling, but Bob, bursting with paternal pride, was not going to miss an opportunity.

"Good! We've not had a broken night's sleep since she left the hospital."

Doc Cruickshank smiled, but only with his lips, I noticed. His eyes remained cool and somewhat pained.

"Aye, always helps. Mine were brats, both of 'em."

Gently he rolled Suzie over onto her back, and then eased her forward, his broad hands spanning her body beneath her little pot belly. She leaned forward so low that her nose flattened on the table between her legs. He propped her back into a sitting position, his hands supporting her beneath the armpits, and then gradually allowed her just enough support to remain still. But she didn't. Again she flopped forward as though the weight of her head were far too much for her little body to cope with. He held a pen in front of her and her tongue reached out to it, but there was no movement in either arm or hand.

I didn't now need to look at Bob to confirm the chill feeling of unease that was seeping through my body. But when concern for the way the older man was allowing her head to flop caused him to edge nearer the table, I observed the tense contours of clenched hands through his pockets. The doctor appeared not to notice either of us. He laid her down, lightly passed his hand across her forehead and tapped her cheek. He almost gave the impression of fumbling, though looking back, I suppose he was searching for the gentlest way of putting it. Only for some reason, he gave up altogether, and made a statement so brutal in its terseness, that I was never to forget it.

"She's mentally retarded." He thrust the words out as if he couldn't wait to be rid of them. "I'm sorry...so very sorry." It was as if he were apologising for a mistake he personally had made.

For some moments the words hovered around, but refused to enter my head, but then pounded in my ears until I felt physically sickened by their repetition.

"You don't mean it do you," I implored. "You aren't certain?"

"Backward?" Bob's voice was a mere horrified whisper. He was willing it not to be true. And then he seemed incapable of uttering another word but remained blanched and speechless.

Doc Cruickshank's voice was choked and husky. "Your little girl is mentally retarded." He did not apologise this time, but stared down at Suzie, her newly learned smile wasted on his grave face. He began to put on her vest - a job that his nurse was normally very adept at taking out of his hands the moment the examination was completed. I suddenly registered that she had not been present in the consulting room tonight. Obviously he had suspected what he was going to have to tell us, and I resented her part in the conspiracy.

"She'll have gone home now," I thought. "I wonder how many other people won't want to see us?" I knew I should take over Suzie's dressing, but my mind was divorced from my body, and I remained on the edge of the chair as he clumsily completed the job.

He always kept a jar of candy on his desk as rewards for those children who suffered injections without complaint, and also because he had an insatiable weakness for old-fashioned humbugs and peppermints. He was taking one out of the wrapping now, and tempted Suzie with its flavour. One tentative lick, and then a more eager one.

"So ye like my peppermints do ye, little one?" It was as if he and she were the only people in the room. "Aye, well just in case you cultivate too great a taste for them, let's try an aniseed." But she demonstrated no obvious enthusiasm.

"Definitely a minty-girl, aye a minty-girl...." Suddenly, for no reason in the world that I could understand, his eyes were smiling again. Bob and I were excluded from something that was simultaneously tragic and special as if we, rather than the dreadful news he had so recently imparted, were the cause of the sheer tension of those moments. He rustled the candy papers, and she gurgled as her tongue sought the taste she had just discovered.

"One more lick," he said "and then we'll all be getting along."
I suppose that having managed to off-load a great weight from his mind, he was waiting for a reaction from Bob and me, but the shock had been so stultifying that we continued to sit as if paralysed.

"I'll come and see you both tomorrow." He put his hand on Bob's shoulder, and left us alone and in that moment I wished he'd said that she was going to die. Mechanically we put on her snowsuit, and silently supporting each other, we took her home. Outer arms pushed the buggy; inner ones were locked around each other. The footsteps we had made earlier, facing the opposite direction, remained unspoilt. Dusk had become darkness whilst we had been at the surgery, and we were grateful for that fact to hide our eyes from passers by who wished us 'goodnight'.

Inside our hall, with the world firmly locked outside, the truth struck with unrelenting force, and we wept uncontrollably. Why had she lived? Why had he waited until we loved her before telling us? And over and over again, why *our* child -why our first baby? WHY?

WHY? How would we ever again know if her smile were one of recognition of us as her parents or just the smile of an.... We could not form the word idiot.

This morning when she had gurgled, seemingly with sheer happiness, what had she really felt? What had she seen? Did she recognise us as the people who bathed her and gave her food? Or were we just anyone? I wondered if she would still have smiled just because she had learned which muscles to use.

The questions, the desperation, the arguing with God, continued through that interminable night. Neither slept. After a while we did not even speak, but stood, one on each side of her cradle, Bob staring almost wildly at the sleeping form of his daughter, and I desperately trying to see something in Suzie that was different from any other baby. My failure to observe one shred of difference served only to increase the tension, the doubt. What *had* Doc Cruickshank seen? What had Suzie done that other babies did not do? Surely not that she had just wobbled over to lick his leather-padded table. She had so far performed according to the book.

At exactly three months, Suzie had presented us with her first smile, and only a week later her eyes had followed a swinging toy attached to her buggy. She was gaining weight and sleeping well.... Sleeping well. I recalled Doc's question. 'Is she gud fer ye?' Yes she slept for long periods, and quite deeply. When Joan and Mike had visited last week, their offspring - a week younger than Suzie - had yelled for over an hour, and Suzie had slept through it all, apparently without even noticing the ruckus.

"Gee you're a lucky son of a bitch," Mike had remarked to Bob. "Our little monster performs like this every time I get home from school." Lucky! I wonder if he'd be so envious now.

My body ached with increasing weariness, but my mind rushed headlong into question after question. Why had nothing been said at the hospital? Who else had noticed? What *was* there to notice? I was aware of Bob taking my hand and leading me to the edge of the bed. We sat there for a long time, with no word being spoken, until finally he said, "I don't want her to live Helen. I can't face that kind of a future."

Although he had been the one to say it, the same thought had occupied both minds.

As with every tragedy, the initial shock was the greatest, because selfish beings that we are, our first reaction is to wonder how a new set of circumstances will affect us personally. The silence was resumed, but not through any decision not to talk. Words beyond those Bob had uttered were so totally inadequate because they couldn't change anything. Time lost all meaning, though I suppose somehow the hours passed.

I do not recall dawn breaking even though we were wide-awake. The cloud of our new knowledge obscured both physical and mental awareness of any further change, and yet with the acceptance that a new day had begun there was some suggestion of relief, even though the relief was born of a possibly false hope that Doc Cruickshank was mistaken in his grave judgement. Doctors didn't know everything. Their mistakes were often in the newspapers. People they had said would die went on living for years. Aggressive feelings towards him increased. He had some nerve stating that a baby had no adult future when she was only three months old. Well he'd live to eat his words about our little Suzie.

I went to the kitchen and boiled her some milk, and Bob, ever suspicious of experts, hovered and scrutinised, whilst I gave her her bottle. She took a long time to drink her seven ounces because she would keep breaking off to smile at us. And with each smile we became more convinced that Doc Cruickshank was getting too old for the job. It was time he handed over to his younger partner. It would take time to forgive him for last night... a long time.... Then we heard his knock at the back door.

He let himself in, leaving his topcoat and over-shoes in the storeroom backing on to the old colonial type kitchen. We stood up and then seemed unable to move to meet him, and with each of his assured steps, our confidence in his mistaken judgement diminished.

He had not been waiting for three months to pass on an idly made decision. He had observed and then bided time until, to his experienced eyes, certainty had come.

"How bad is she?" Bob asked, wasting time on neither pleasantries nor preamble.

Doc Cruickshank shook his head non-committtally, and then in gentler tones than he had been able to summon the previous evening, "You'll need a specialist to answer ye that one."

A combination of misery and consternation caused me to ask, "Then how..?" but he took up the question, his face tired and drawn, as though feeling himself the pain that the voicing of his words inflicted.

"How did I know at all eh?" He looked at me for several moments, and then at our daughter, with a measure of sympathy and understanding I was rarely to see in anyone again. Taking her left hand he pointed to a continuous line across her palm. "Look at yours," he directed, "broken on both hands."

"Oh but surely that could mean anything." Bob's tone was little short of derisive. "Only fortune tellers resort to such things."

Ignoring the remark he said, "Remember how you came to see her on the third day or so? I asked you how she was and you replied, "Oh fine - and the cheeky little minx even put her tongue out at me."

"Oh she does that alright - just look at her now." For a moment my husband's bitterness disappeared and he regarded his baby as he had prior to the visit to the surgery.

"Well ye see the wee one has rather a lot of tongue to accommodate. It's not surprising she gives up on occasion and lets it peep out."

On reflection I had not been aware of this - had I assumed that all babies did it, or was I just unobservant? I stole a glance at her, somehow afraid and tense. She still appeared to be much like any other baby. I knew that twenty-four hours ago, I would have added 'Except that she's ten times more beautiful.' But now I was guarded. Perhaps she wasn't pretty -maybe she just had a lovely skin and being baby-warm-and-soft, I assumed she was appealing. Could it be that one day she would be unattractive, go on, say it, ugly, because there was no light in her eyes?

And then I heard his voice again, low and controlled now.

"You said you sometimes had to waken her to take food?"

I nodded, because words were all frozen up again.

"Aye, it's the kind of placidity that is characteristic of the mongol child. It's often inert and happily spends the day in a manner that would cause another little mite to holler with boredom."

It did not escape me that he had said 'it' and not 'he' or 'she'.

"What exactly does 'mongol' mean?" My mind seemed to tighten as if refusing to absorb any more hurt.

"A special kind of retarded child - easily recognisable, for all mongol children look somewhat alike."

Whilst continuing to look at Doc Cruickshank, out of the corner of my eye, I saw Bob flinch.

"Incidentally," Doc continued, "mongol children are the most affectionate of types."

How awful. She was going to be affectionate and demonstrative, and we wouldn't be able to return that love. But I said only, "I hadn't realised - possibly because I've never been interested - that retarded children could be classified into groups."

"No, most people never give it a thought. Kids to them are clever, average or stupid. Few people have occasion to consider it further. Too few people care." He seemed to be talking aloud now without realising it. "I wish to God that one day soon the world will accept that one is as deserving of our time as another."

"Will people refer to our baby as stupid?" asked Bob abrasively, and I knew that Doc wished he had used a gentler word. But he didn't deny it.

"Some who are too ignorant to be worth your bothering about."

"I can't do it. You know that don't you?"

The confession tumbled out. I expected him to slap my face to prevent an outburst of hysteria. But I did not feel hysterical; only totally inadequate to cope with this mountain of responsibility that had so unexpectedly presented itself. Weakness swept through me as I finally succumbed and accepted the statement that last night had changed our world. The sheer misery was unendurable.

"I can't do it. I can't." I was unashamed and uncaring of the tears streaming down my face and made no attempt to wipe them. "I'm just not good enough…. Haven't got the courage."

His voice was low and gruff when he finally spoke. He took both my hands in his own.

"You'll allow me to be the judge of that," he said. "As Chairman of the School Board, I've got to know Bob pretty well - perhaps rather better than he'd like! Difficult cuss on occasions." He endeavoured to reduce the tension by assuming everyday banter – "but solid as a rock, and not one to be thrown by circumstances. And I think Helen, that I've got the measure of you too." His tone became very matter-of-fact. And some of my ice-cold tension began to thaw.

"Now the first thing to remember is that you are not going to cope with this thing alone. You and Bob together will have charge of this wee mite, and you'll give each other strength. And there will be others to call on."

I did not need to glance at Bob to know that he doubted this attributed strength as much as I.

"Specialised knowledge will be available to you when you need it." Then he gazed down at the carpet before addressing the two of us authoritatively. "If after two months, you continue to feel as you do now, then you come and tell me. You'll need to have no shame or embarrassment - just say. Tell me how you feel - how you both feel - and we'll go from there."

"I'll tell you now how I feel, Doc," Bob's delivery was hard, but characteristically direct. His ashen countenance made him appear a decade older than yesterday.

"I'm feeling it would have been kinder to let Suzie die. What sort of future do you think you medics have given her?" And then, "I'm sorry," he apologised immediately. "It was we who gave her life, not you. But surely when you knew, you could have, well, let something happen?"

"I'll answer your first question." Doc was angry. "Life is yours to give to her Bob. Yours and Helen's. Not mine, nor the staff who delivered her except insofar as we are part of the society in which she'll live."

Inexplicably I felt calmer, though I didn't understand why, and I asked, "When did it happen? I mean I wasn't ill during my pregnancy."

"No, it was decided when she was conceived. The tragedy is that all through the nine months there was no way of knowing, or doing anything about it. And as for bringing her into the world alive Bob, you know full well that that is what every doctor is pledged to do. We're men, not the Almighty to decide who shall live and who will die. A greater power than our own decides that. If it makes you feel better, blame Him. I daresay his shoulders are broad enough to take a few home truths. I've been guilty of passing some on to him in my time."

Before he left, he gave us the name of a paediatrician in London, Ontario. "I've made an appointment for ye on Thursday week. He's a good man – well respected."

"There doesn't seem to be much use in getting a second opinion." Bob's bitterness had not subsided. "You've found all the pointers."

"Enough to tell there's no doubt about the mongolism," Doc said gently, "but I don't have the expertise to indicate the degree of retardation."

"Isn't it enough that she *is* - without knowing the degree?"

"Enough for today, aye." He enclosed Suzie's hand in his own. "I know it seems so unfair, but when the whole situation becomes less tragic to you, you'll want to know how best to help her. I'll be on my way now." His deep grey, usually so matter-of-fact eyes glistened a little as he left the room.

CHAPTER TWO

Doctor Cruickshank's new assistant and his wife Carol lived in our partner semi. The two halves had originally been one large colonial house first owned by our landlady's grandparents. One could reasonably assume from the appearance of the house that the family fortunes had steadily dwindled over the past decade, for it was by far the shabbiest house in the row. Shabby or not, it provided us with a roof over our heads, a vast, as yet unkempt garden (backyard to the Canadians) and the blissful freedom of nine large rooms in each half.

Most evenings since our respective babies had been born, found us enjoying a hand or two of bridge. On summer evenings we played on the shared veranda outside the two nurseries and where the shade kept the mosquitoes away.

Few Canadians adopt the attitude that a new baby is reason to stay home of an evening, especially when the infant is still at the stage of virtually sleeping around the clock and just waking for nourishment. They accept invitations readily, and armed with a bottle of feed, a couple of diapers and a polythene bag for the laundry, take junior along to share the host's nursery, alongside any resident infants.

Bridge was played fairly keenly until heated arguments on the correctness or otherwise, of the bidding, would cause divorce to become a likely prospect, and then someone would suggest that the cards be discarded in favour of a long, cool beer. Sooner or later

11

discussion would revolve around our mutual landlady who was kindness itself, but whose choice of wallpaper was diabolical.

One took a calculated risk in persuading her that a room required redecorating, for along with her acquiescence, appeared umpteen rolls of even more flamboyant wallpaper than the one we had learned to live with until now. Too late to bemoan the fact that of the two we preferred the one whose dinginess, through longevity, obscured at least the brilliance of its original design, and so more and more of our walls sported huge cascades of roses in full bloom. We had once suggested painting over them in a bland magnolia but her genteel protests silenced us for the length of our tenancy.

"Oh no dears, we don't want to lose the character of the dear old house do we?"

We agreed we did not!

We hadn't played since being told about our daughter's retardation, though for obvious reasons Tom would have been cognisant of the circumstances. In fact we hadn't been to see anyone since finding out. I don't know if we were embarrassed or ashamed, or both - it did feel rather as if we had committed some sort of crime and were lying low. Not a decision we had taken consciously: it just happened that way. Even so, I wanted terribly to find out what was involved. I needed to know what a mongol child did that others did not do - or perhaps the reverse was more relevant in view of the limitations.

I didn't want to visit the reference library, so the only way to find the answers was to search in Tom's medical books. Ascertaining that my daughter was fast asleep, I slipped around to put my request to Carol. She hesitated momentarily and then withdrew the 'M' volume from the shelf.

"I suppose this is what you want?"

I nodded, not trusting myself to speak.

"Is it wise Helen?" she asked dutifully though with no discernible conviction. We had been friends for too long for her to pretend I was doing something she wouldn't have done in the same circumstances.

"I may as well know what I'm up against" I didn't intend the curtness, but suddenly became enveloped in shame as I watched little Caroline sitting up in her high chair. What had happened to make one pregnancy end in tragedy and another in such carefree joy? Carol and I had gone through our pregnancies in similar fashion it seemed, though we hadn't known each other so well at the beginning.

Both of us had been pretty healthy specimens and continued to live normally, if increasingly clumsily in the last weeks. Yet here was Caroline, to all appearances a perfect baby with a bright future. And all I had brought into the world was a little bundle of protoplasm destined to be one of its vegetables. It was like learning you had failed an exam, when since you had written it you'd been certain you had made the honours class.

"Helen, I'm sorry...it's rotten luck. I can't imagine what I would feel like..." Carol said, obviously feeling she ought to say something.

"I'm not sure either," I stammered. "How I feel, I mean. It hasn't quite sunk in yet."

"Tom says if it had happened to me, he would never have allowed me to see the baby. I wonder why they let you nurse her?"

So they had discussed our Minty and evidently would not have elected to keep such a baby. A tension settled in my throat.

"I hadn't thought about it from an official angle," I admitted. "Perhaps they weren't sure at first, or maybe it had something to do with having a British passport." I had read somewhere that the BMA had a different slant on taking babies away from their mothers at birth.

"I'm not very clear about anything anymore." The confession tumbled out. "I just don't understand. If fate decreed that it was my turn for something awful to happen, why couldn't I have been paralysed, or killed in a road accident or something? Why did Minty have to get it?"

"Gee Helen, it's not like that. Things happen sometimes. Even thousand to one chances." And then she asked abruptly, "Why did you call her Minty, then? I thought you had decided on Suzanne?"

"Oh, a stupid reason really. Doc Cruickshank discovered she loves old-fashioned humbugs, and called her a minty-girl. Somehow it has stuck."

Deep down I was wondering whether that was the real reason. Or did the different name represent a different baby? On that fateful evening that already seemed an eternity ago we had set out to keep a routine appointment for a little girl called Suzanne...a little girl who might one day be a ballet dancer, a barrister or dress designer. And on that same evening we had returned without her. Instead we had brought home another child who would be none of those things, whose life would be narrow and limited, destined to be one of nature's outcasts. No, Suzanne didn't exist anymore, but Minty did, and somehow her needs had to be met.

Assuming Carol had heard my thoughts, I said, "I just have to get started.... I must know what she is, even if only in cold clinical terms. I'll take the book if I may for a while Carol...I'll bring it back before Tom gets home for lunch."

She appeared troubled and hesitant. "Wouldn't you rather stay here for a coffee, and we'll look at it together?"

"Thanks all the same, but if I'm going to get emotional I'd rather do it without an audience."

Carol nodded as I left; she seemed hurt, but I didn't know what to do, and once home, I recoiled into myself.

I could only glance perfunctorily at Minty, for that's what she had become, before turning up the word mongolism. And immediately I wished I had taken time to prepare myself. Sometimes, by imagining a hideous situation just before you think one is about to arise, then the reality doesn't seem so bad by comparison, and that in itself is comforting.

But I had not gone through any such process, and now my eyes were held by the reproduction of a photograph: a photograph of a little girl though her sex was meaningless. Her hair hung straight and fringed; her eyes set only superficially in a deadpan face that seemed to be gazing into a space just short of the camera. My instinctive reaction was to slam the book closed, but the sheer horror within me had an almost hypnotic effect. I covered each part of the print in turn, and tried to imagine the difference a new hairstyle would make. To cut it short would only emphasize the overlarge puffy cheeks, and if allowed to grow it would become messy and tangled if her mother were not constantly on hand to tidy it. Why had I said 'her mother' and not I? And couldn't she be trained not to allow her tongue to loll forward? However much, or little, I covered the photograph, I could find no suggestion of light in her eyes, or expression in her face. And yet Minty's eyes sparkled - each time she smiled. They had, hadn't they? Now I wasn't sure.

I looked from the book to Minty, and felt terribly, desperately alone. I must check her carefully now; take each point of the photograph in turn. Above all I must endeavour to be an outsider and systematically list all the salient facts from the accompanying text. But still, as far as the photograph was concerned, there was, for me, no resemblance at all between Minty and that little girl. A tantalising hope returned. Maybe Doc Cruickshank had made a mistake. Maybe it had all been one long miserable nightmare, and she really was still Suzie after all.

I raced through the text dwelling only on highly relevant details. 'They all look alike' I read. They were extremely loving, and inclined to be over-affectionate. All right, but this was still pertaining to other children, mongol children, and so far I hadn't read anything to connect them with Suzie.

Abruptly the hope faded. I read more slowly now for the text was almost a replica of my own diary in my baby's first months....silent babies...little tendency to cry even when a feed is late or withheld...usually sleep with the head way back. And then Doc Cruickshank's description of the continuous line across the palm .....a tongue so long that the mouth had difficulty in accommodating it.

She did not wake as I lifted her from her crib, and kissed her eyelids. "Little Minty," I sobbed. "Who are you?"

I pushed the book aside, and wished with all my heart I had not perused its contents. Minty did not remotely resemble that child, but from now on I would be waiting for her to change, until one day I would see the uniform expression on her face, and know with certainty that she was one of them.

I sat with her in my arms in the silent world she seemed to create, and felt no compunction to open the book again. Whatever I had to learn now I must learn first hand from Minty herself, and certainly more gradually, and in smaller doses than that which I had just consumed.

Quite unaware of time, I mused awhile, and recalled seeing a boy in town - I couldn't remember where - he was much like the photograph, only older, considerably older. Obviously I had done precious little to be pleasant to him or to his parents, who one day long ago must have felt as Bob and I did now, or I would have remembered him more clearly.

I glanced at the clock and knew that Carol would be getting anxious about the return of the book before Tom came home. Minty opened her eyes as I put her back onto the soft blankets and smiled up at me. Though I gazed intently, I could see no mongolism there.

"Won't be long pet. Don't cry while I'm gone." and as I picked up the hefty volume added, "Oh if only you would."

Carol was cooking when I went in so I replaced the book myself.

"Did you find what you wanted?"

"Rather what I didn't want," I replied. "Enough to be going on with." I looked directly at her. "I'm going to ask you something, and if you're the friend I think you are, you'll give me a straight answer."

I wanted her to say something....anything....to react to the question I felt so inadequate to ask. But she was steeling herself to comply with the request I was courageous enough to make. That courage was already in doubt, but, since no response was forthcoming, I pressed on and asked, "If Tom hadn't seen the surgery records, would you have known? I mean, does Minty look different? Is she...?"

She nodded. The reply was superfluous, but because I had attached the degree of friendship to it, she said, "Yes Helen, I guess we'd have known. But not so easily as with some."

"Thanks," I choked. "Be seeing you. No, don't see me out."

Back with Minty, I suddenly yearned for some air. Stupid in a place where there was nothing but fresh air. I longed desperately for an English wood where I could sit, think, and ask myself some pretty fundamental questions. But though there were miles and miles of space between these minute Canadian 'towns' - often as few as eight hundred people in each, - separated by hundreds of miles of highway, parks or woods inside the towns did not exist. If one walked to where houses came to an end, the only thing left to do was to walk along the single highway out of the town for it would be foolhardy to enter the 'bush' on either side - dense, coniferous forests where it was so easy to lose one's sense of direction. Even experienced hunters went out in groups to stalk the deer.

But we would go out any way, I resolved. As soon as she had finished her feed, we would go and find some sort of peace and tranquillity. Peace. I put my finger into Minty's hand, and she gripped it without moving or waking. What a thing to search for when here it was in this tiny girl; so much of it, that she didn't even protest when, because of the morning's research, I was late with her lunch. No, it wasn't just peace I wanted, but an existence without the 'rotten luck' elements. And like most other souls on this planet, I obviously couldn't have it.

Life, cold and unrelenting did not owe me happiness or protection from hurt and pain. This much I could, and would, accept. But how could I ever accept that life had no debts to Minty? It had sent her into the world with such an immense handicap; how would the balance ever be recovered? What recompense could ever be offered as compensation. And how in heaven's name had I reached the age of twenty-four with no clear understanding of mongolism? Where had I been, and whom had I passed by? How many such children had gained no smile or greeting from me - only distaste and repulsion.

I reflected how I must have put my hand in my pocket to contribute to the handicapped without a shred of feeling beyond irritation when hastening along a busy High Street. And the utter normality of my life suddenly sickened me. I had never once had to face up to tragedy; death had not yet touched me; no important exam had ever been failed. My progress to qualified schoolteacher had been painlessly, comfortably gradual and without setback...And now here I was, utterly unequipped to assume the awful responsibility of caring for another person's abnormal life.

How many miles I walked in those early weeks, I have no recollection, only a vague impression of fruitless searching, for I discovered only one solitary fact. Life apparently sometimes forbids running away.

CHAPTER THREE

We were emotionally very close in those early weeks, somehow paralysed into an acceptance and understanding of the brittleness in each other. Affinity, strengthened by disaster, and even more by the tenacious illogical refusal to believe in it, we spent endless hours just holding hands, peering at her crib in the silent world Minty seemed to create, our minds numb.

In the daytime, Bob's responsibility to his students produced an outward demeanour that was mere facade, but at night, released of the necessity to conceal the guilt and shame that enveloped us, we lay locked in each others arms. Together, yet distant, we were unable to discuss the frightening vista opening ahead of us. Each privately grieving, we were yet undesirous of the intimacy that had resulted in this raw, unmanageable nightmare. That one minute chromosome could result in such disproportionate obligation, was too much for the mind to absorb - but nevertheless occupied it to the exclusion of all else.

During the two weeks we were to wait for our appointment with the paediatrician, I was conscious of a constant seesawing of my emotions. I would gaze at my daughter in horror and dismay, and then almost immediately, utterly without belief in her condition, would hug her and smother her soft face with my kisses. At other times I would be coldly conscious of a desperate effort to withdraw my love and, angry at my failure to do so, would grow irritable and taciturn.

I took her out as little as possible, offering the bitter cold as an excuse. To bush-Canadians who lived with deep snow from October to April each year, this must indeed have sounded little short of moronic, and to those who knew it was an excuse, offensive too, for needing to have an excuse meant that I distanced myself from their natural good neighbourliness and genuine community spirit.

I asked Bob to pick up the mail from our cubicle at the central mailing office. Having no postman to make individual house deliveries, and therefore no letterbox, was one of the differences to which I had had to become accustomed. And now I deliberately deprived myself of the daily walk to the Main Street, in the expectation of a letter from England. We did not talk about this change in our routine. It was as if Bob not only understood, but would have made the same request of me were he the one to stay at home to care for our baby.

When the necessity to collect groceries forced me to venture forth, it was always with the buggy hood pulled up, and the eiderdown partially concealing her. I was hideously ashamed and so glad of the heavy snowfall, which enabled me to use my upturned collar and downward glance as an excuse for not seeing people with whom I would normally have stopped to pass pleasantries.

The Red Front Grocery Store and the Butcher's shop were only ten minutes walk away from the house, and I took to visiting them as dusk was falling. One particular evening, after I had left the High Street and was hurriedly turning into Frances Street, I pulled up sharply to prevent the buggy bumping into someone in the shadows. Whoever it was became aware of my presence and awkwardly changed his weight from one foot to the other, and as he did so, the street lamp illuminated his face. Swiftly I put up my hand to stifle a horrified gasp. It was the mongol boy I had once seen in town. Now beside his mother, I remembered that his family kept the Hardware Store on the corner by the library. He was Jimmy McMahon. He made no reaction when the buggy had almost bumped into him, except to gaze at me as if I were a strange object that had passed into his field of vision. His long tongue rolled, and his expressionless eyes were almost lost in the smooth, podgy contours of his face.

Although he reached her shoulder, Mrs McMahon swiftly and instinctively put her arm around him as protectively as if he were an infant, "Careful dear...look where you are going" And then, "Oh Mrs Wade it's you. Well there now, how fortunate, we have only just left your house. But we thought you wouldn't be far away."

My voice froze in my throat; to reply was impossible. She had brought that boy...or man, it was difficult to tell, to my house. I was to smile and say sociable things, and invite them to come again. As if from some immense distance, I heard my own voice, high pitched and stumbling. "I'm so sorry, but I must rush....I'm in such a hurry."
She was taken aback. "Oh but I only wanted to say..."

"Please don't say how sorry you are," I stammered. "I couldn't bear it."

"Sorry. For what?"
My mind reeled momentarily, and I felt she was derisive of what I suddenly realised was my over-ample self-pity.

"I beg your pardon –I really must go."

"Go where?" she insisted gently. "You think that by forever running, you'll run away from your problem too? You know that's impossible. You love her too much already."
I was aware of a great inner strength - hers, not mine. She looked hard at me, as if she were feeling the very fibre of which I was made.

"Please go away," my thoughts were pleading silently, and to my shame she received them as if I had spoken aloud.

"Goodnight my dear. You are quite right. It's none of my business. I just thought we could share what must have once seemed a pretty remote experience. Goodnight."

"Goodnight," I whispered hoarsely. "I'm sorry."

An experience! Is that all she considered it? And that awful boy! There was shame attached to my repulsion, but even stronger was the inability to reverse my reactions. I rushed headlong towards

21

home, refusing to couple Minty with the boy on whom I had turned my back so abruptly - a boy so fat and vacant, only half alive and aware, and oh God so very, very ugly. Was Minty really going to be like that, because if she was, I had to go right now to Doc Cruickshank and tell him I couldn't do it. I wasn't the type. I didn't have that kind of metal. Please let her die. Oh please God, let her die!

But Minty didn't die. She gained a further three ounces, smiled more smiles, and grew, to my prejudiced and confused eyes daily more lovely. The doubts were still there, and we knew that in spite of all our initial reactions, we did want a second opinion. We were ready, or as ready as we would ever be to absorb the degree of retardation.

I hadn't yet written to England to break the news to still excited grandparents. How did one set about explaining that their first grandchild had no other future than that of a vegetable? Bad enough face to face...but by airmail....No, on second thoughts it might be easier. They wouldn't see my tears, nor I theirs.

Bob had driven over to a school fifty kilometres away for a Science Department meeting, so we had planned a later evening meal than usual. "Why can't we get on with the job without forever pontificating about it?" he had grumbled before leaving, partly out of impatience, and partly because I knew he didn't appreciate that whilst he was a 'natural', there were those, who by virtue of regular meetings and feedback, were still endeavouring to become good teachers. I knew exactly what his response would have been if I had put this to him: "You can't learn how to teach at meetings - you just do it!"

Communication was never a problem for Bob and his own total lack of shyness and out-going personality enabled him to get to know the person below the surface very quickly - an asset that served him well both in teaching and later in business.

"You take too much notice of what people say," he would tell me. "Find out why they are saying it ...watch how they behave."

I expected he would also call on Arne, his best friend and sparring partner, whilst over there. Arnold taught Science, and his wife Jill had been a school secretary until their marriage. She was away in Toronto now spending time with her mother following her father's death. They had often struck me as a strange couple; Jill so gentle and unassuming, shy too, though not to the point of finding it difficult to get along with people, almost everyone in fact. Arnold, on the other hand, was a dynamic intellectual whose unfortunate ability it was to give others the impression that he displayed his own intellect in order to highlight their lesser degree of it. He didn't suffer fools gladly and rarely managed to hide the fact he found most of his colleagues boring. Not, as he always went to some length to emphasize, boring beyond endurance, but certainly boring to a point where he openly grudged them the time he gave them.

To Jill, good manners deemed it not only desirable but essential not to leave people with this impression, and it was the cause of much tension between them. Only one other thing was guaranteed to cause temperatures to rise even higher, and that was Arnold's burning ambition to visit, and possibly to live in, Israel: to visit the land of his forebears before he was too old to find the effort arduous.

Jill, in fact, had never actually refused to go to Israel in spite of Arnold's protest that he would 'go on his own one day by God'. I suspected that what she really objected to was the fact that he was always making it a talking point and bone of contention, whilst displaying no actual evidence of a determination to put the plan into action. One almost felt that he wished he had been persecuted so that the case for going back to his roots was stronger. In actual fact few people knew or cared that he was of Jewish descent. In the small north Canadian towns to which people of almost every nationality had immigrated, a man's origin was rarely a case for invective.

I had frequently observed Jill, her discomfort growing as Arnold would expostulate on a new scheme put forward by the Head, or the Science Department's plans for curriculum development, or the most recent decision taken by the Board of Governors. She appeared to recognise, and credit, her husband's courage to be outspoken in preference to going along with the crowd, but the recognition of it did not automatically create the admiration she would like to have felt. Perhaps because he didn't have the knack of putting his views over in such a way as to give others a lead to express their own sentiments on the subject in question, but rather forced them back into a general opposition to the man himself.

But I had also watched her when he wasn't protesting, or holding forth; when they were at a party or dance, just enjoying each other's company. With Jill his sole audience, Arnold would recount a conversation or article he had read, and she, understanding all or nothing of it, would have eyes only for this tactless effervescent man she had been fool enough to marry.

I had mused long enough to get no further with my letter than the date when I heard Bob kicking off his overboots.

"Hi, anyone home?"

"No, I left you a couple of hours ago," I called out, pleased that his arrival gave me an excuse to defer writing.

"Really! All the more supper for me then! How's Minty?" Momentarily I wondered whether I'd ever be able to say 'Oh she's driven me to distraction all day,' but I just said "Fine."

Bob threw his jacket over a chair, hungrily munched on an apple, and then said, Arnold and Jill won't hear of our hiring a car next weekend. They've got their Christmas shopping to do and say they may as well do it in London as anywhere."

"But I thought Jill wasn't due home until the weekend."

"She wasn't, but she is. I went with Arnold to pick her up at the station."

"Three wasn't a crowd," I teased.

"Well yes, it was actually."

Bob's words surprised me. He went on. "Funny really. I never imagined Arnold being the type to show someone he had missed her. Obviously had though. I felt tactless to say the least for not suggesting I cleared off, but he insisted I went along. Anyway, for reasons best known to herself, she's back early. Seems she has come in to a nice little inheritance."

"So maybe they'll go to Israel after all." I spoke more as a continuation of my thoughts in Bob's absence than as a reply.

"I wonder why that idea came so readily to mind - has Arne mentioned it again recently?"

"No, I was considering them whilst you were out, and wondering whether Arnold's insistence on going was based on a real desire, or on the fact that he believes Jill is opposed to it."

"You mean she isn't?"

"Oh I don't go as far as to say the idea would have occurred to her if she hadn't been married to Arnold but I suspect if they did go, Jill's enjoyment of the country would exceed Arne's."

"Maybe. Anyway the subject didn't arise today. He was far too engrossed in a painting he bought at an auction."

"Really. Did you like it?"

"Not really my style. Bloody diabolical in fact, but Arnold obviously gets a kick out of it. Sees all sorts of things in it. How I wish I had his breadth of vision."

"You don't do so badly yourself," and he grinned in response to my feeding of his vanity. "There doesn't seem to be much that leaves you apathetic either. There aren't many stones that remain unturned between the pair of you."

"Maybe not, but just look at the way he handles that fiddle. For a chap whose specialist subject is Science, I reckon he knows more about the arts than the rest of the staff put together."

Unknown to each other, they had each left their respective countries to set out for Canada, without the security of knowing anyone, or having pre-arranged jobs to go to: Arnold because to him, Canada was another promised land on which one day he might make an impact, and Bob because he was young, newly graduated and unafraid, and ready to see the world.

He had taken something of a jolt when he first discovered the much wider difference between rich and poor than had existed in the

UK and was rapidly forced into taking a job as a tie salesman in a Toronto department store, and with the resulting pay, able only to rent one dingy basement room. Whilst the pay may have covered the rent, it didn't do much more, and down to his last dollars he replied to an advertisement for a teaching post in a tiny gold-mining community in the north Ontario wilderness, Red Lake. Because of the immense distance involved, he was hired over the 'phone. Thankfully with the promise of a job, came a travel allowance to enable him to make the thousand mile journey from Toronto to Red Lake.

Independently, I had just arrived from England myself, much less spectacularly, having been interviewed at the Canadian Embassy, and provided with a sea passage from Liverpool to Montreal from where I took a two day journey by railroad to an equally small town where I was to teach at the high school. There was quite an adjustment to be made having previously spent two years in London where I had taken full advantage of theatres and galleries. Here, one cinema showing films a year after they were seen in Toronto, constituted the total public entertainment for the town of eight hundred people.

Feeling culturally starved I could not have looked forward more to the Teachers Convention at which 'my' school would be host to all the schools in northern Ontario. The headmaster thought it would be 'kind o cute' to have an English accent on reception duty, and thus I was stationed in the Entrance Hall.

Amongst all the Canadians I could not help but pick up the sound of a Lancashire voice in a group chatting nearby, and was delighted when its owner, Bob, asked me where to locate a call box for someone requiring mechanical assistance before driving the three hundred three miles back to Red Lake after the conference.

We couldn't honestly say we paid much attention to the convention over those four days and agreed that to see each other again we would meet at Kenora, a mid way point in the three hundred miles that separated our two schools.

A year later we were married, and in June when the school year ended, we reluctantly said Goodbye to the tiny northern communities of which we had been part. We travelled the long journey south to Toronto and rented temporary accommodation whilst Bob completed a post degree ten-week summer course and from there we moved to a small town even by Canadian standards, for him to take up his new post in the Autumn term, and where we would await our first baby.

Simultaneously Arnold had joined the staff as Head of the Science Department at a neighbouring school. And so began the friendship between the two men, drawn together at first by the lack of a Canadian background and then for all time because of the interests they shared and the mental sparring each provided for the other. Bob continued to sing Arnold's praises and I smiled at his admiration; set in the same mould, he was one of the very few Arnold failed to antagonise.

"I don't honestly think he takes his Jewish background any more seriously than we do. Any way damn good of them to take us down to London." Bob said.

I verbally registered appreciation of their thought, but now that the appointment for Minty's assessment was only days away, a vain hope that something would prevent us from going was increasing. With transport now organised, it seemed inevitable that we should visit a perfect stranger to whom we would display a much less than perfect baby. The enforced acceptance of the situation threw me near to despair and I was unreasonably taciturn during supper.

"Having second thoughts about keeping the appointment?" Bob's full gaze irritated me.

"I just wonder if it's absolutely necessary? After all, we know she's retarded: what does the degree matter?"

"I know that if we don't go, you'll forever wonder what it was we might have been told."

I recognised that now we'd got on to the subject of Minty, Bob was as depressed as I, but I still couldn't stop myself admitting that on Saturday of all days, I didn't want company.

"I know they've offered for the best of reasons Bob, but honestly, I'd really rather we were on our own - even if it means going by train."

"Why Helen?" He knew that he was forcing an answer that once voiced, may lose its edge.

I merely reiterated my objection. "I just don't want anyone else around; not even friends."

"You mean you don't want them to see our baby. Helen we can't cut ourselves off from the world because Minty isn't normal."

"That's not true," I protested. But it was. I was ashamed of her; ashamed of the baby we had produced together. And then I felt ashamed of my shame, and endeavoured to justify myself. "I don't want to answer lots of questions."

"Helen, Minty is Nature's mistake. Not yours or mine. The sooner you accept that, the healthier it's going to be for all of us."

"You sound as if you've been talking to Doctor Cruickshank."

"Oh?"

"I have. Helen, he insists that if you can't accept Minty's mongolism, you are not to feel there is anything wrong in having her brought up in a home." His face lost some of the strain as the words were uttered.

"Oh he does, does he? Well the next time you and he are putting the world to rights, you might inform him that I've no intention of having her brought up in any other house than this one."

This determined outburst shook me to the core; I refused to believe it was I who had spoken. In that moment I had made a commitment, and simultaneously taken on one hell of a fight.

Bob smiled; the sort of smile he wore when he had won an argument, only there was no triumph on his face, just relief. "Well, having made your decision, perhaps you'll be willing to share her a little instead of trying to fight a lone battle. When I get home each evening I don't want to find the two of you locked up in the house together as if the rest of the world had ceased to exist. "We'll start by sharing her with Jill and Arnold."

I made the coffee without responding. I still didn't want them to come along. But I knew Bob was right, and I also knew that he'd spoken to himself as much as to me. He had given me advice. Now I hoped he would give me time. What hell had he gone through these past days? Selfishly, I hadn't asked. Being the one to stay at home, I had assumed I was suffering alone. Yet every time he looked at a pretty student in his class he must have tortured himself with the thought that his own daughter would never grow up to be attractive to men. There would never be wedding bells or grandchildren or the natural cycle of life being renewed. I poured a second cup. What on earth was I doing thinking of wedding bells? She was only four months old!

CHAPTER FOUR

By dawn on Saturday we were packed into the Volkswagen Beetle, muffled in overcoats, and travelling the sleek, white road to London. We were all aware that beneath the gleaming whiteness of the new fall of snow, lay a continuous sheet of ice. No one spoke a great deal, so that Arnold could concentrate fully on the conditions, and for my own part because I could think of nothing but the impending interview. Musing, I decided the situation was something like waiting to meet one's maker, offering for commendation the fruits of one's life, and for retribution one's failures and shortcomings. Except of course, I had no doubt that the man I was about to meet would be too polite to mention failures. I wondered what his approach would be; patronising perhaps, prefacing every sentence with the royal we, as if he were part of the ....part of what? Mistake merely? Or just plain inadequacy, that seemed even worse because of the innocuous nature of it.

I realised that Bob was nudging me into an awareness that Jill was posing a question. She was enquiring about our plans for the vacation.

"Christmas?" I repeated giving myself a brief moment to consider. "I don't know...we've no definite plans." Plans were things we made before our world had come to such an abrupt halt.

"Why don't you two come over for Christmas dinner?"
I marvelled suddenly at my own audacity. Of course, they wouldn't want to come. It would all be too embarrassing. How different from

all my previous years when November had been an exciting lead-up to the best time of the year. Christmas with turkey, a tree and friends dropping in; phone calls from England. The month had passed and I had been oblivious of the days as separate entities. Only a blurred greyness preceded our journey today. I stole a second or two to consider what Christmas would be like this year and knew it would be what every other day in the last weeks had been: a little mongol girl, and a huge question mark. Oh God, how would I ever cope?

Through the fog of my desperation I heard Jill insisting that no, we should go to their place because they'd got a party organised, but, of course, they'd drop by on Christmas morning to bring Minty her gift. Oh how transparent she was. They would dutifully come and see Minty when there was no one else around, and then we would go to their party and meet all their friends whilst a sitter cared for Minty to avoid any awkward scenes. But who on earth would want to sit with a mongol child?

"You tell me that Jill," I pleaded as if she had been party to my thoughts. "You tell me who would."

I felt Bob hastily take a firm hold of my wrist and apologise for my outburst, though of course, he himself had no idea of the thought that had consumed my concentration. He explained the strain I had been under, which only served to increase my guilt, for hadn't he been equally affected? I wanted to cry out that it wasn't a strain that the passing of time would cure, but a tragedy that would last all my life. But how could they understand when even Bob didn't. I surrendered to a consuming fatigue and leaned back onto the seat.

"I'm so sorry." I offered my apology without any excuses.

Arnold immediately came to my rescue. "Feasting our souls on the surrounding beauty is all very well folks, but I need to satisfy the inner man. Next roadhouse we'll pull in for pancakes. Okay?"

Coffee and syrup pancakes was a traditional Canadian breakfast, and we enjoyed some of the best before setting out again to become part of the now increasing traffic into a community that closely resembled a provincial English town. The wild expansive beauty was behind us. Oh how I had come to love it, ever since I had arrived from England almost three years ago. It had been strange at first and difficult to adjust to a country that had no apparent past.

No Norman churches or medieval castles. No Elizabethan pubs or picturesque villages; only straggling settlements with gas stations and drive-ins, breakfast bars and drug-stores, and long, long distances between one community and another. Distances of three hundred miles and more between schools so that a baseball match involved a whole weekend of travel and lodging with members of the opposing team. Indeed Red Lake was so remote that the only road into it was also the road out. To go further north, one travelled by plane, not by car. And the school at which I had taught was the one to which Bob often brought a baseball team. At least the year we met, we contrived the matches so that his students were frequent visitors!

Delighted by the opportunity for trips away from the tight community in which they lived up there in the 'bush', they feigned ignorance of the real reason behind them, and were amused by our attempt to convince them that our meetings were wholly for professional reasons.

Here in the London, Ontario, Canada lost its identity again. We could have been almost anywhere. Supermarkets, flats, teeming traffic, and ordinary every-day people going about their business. No one could ever describe the people in the north as ordinary. Many of them were of East European origin; some had come to Canada as refugees from oppressive governments, whilst others had come in search of adventure; all had that inner strength of people who had learned to cope, compromise and live with the elements of Canada's untamed environs.

We pulled into the sidewalk to study a street map, and discovered we were no more than a mile from the address we had been given. Arnold had no difficulty in finding it, and he slid to a halt, almost reverently I thought, at an imposing front door. We agreed a time and place to meet for a meal before tackling the journey home. I noticed

Arnold touch Bob's shoulder as we got out of the car, and Bob acknowledged his friend's understanding with a tight-lipped nod. I felt Jill's eyes follow us up the seven stone steps, and it was some seconds before the engine revved, and they set off for their Christmas shopping.

We rang the bell and almost immediately the wide door was opened.

"You can go straight in," the receptionist smiled. "Mr Baker is expecting you."

She opened a further door into his consulting room, and a tall, but physically unimpressive man, got up to greet us. As he spoke, I felt instinctively I must believe every word he uttered, for he gave an immediate impression of cool efficiency and utter competence. Not soft and kindly as Doc Cruickshank, who undoubtedly lagged a little behind the rapid advance of medicine as he drew near to retirement. The expensive apparatus and equipment that surrounded this doctor, in addition to a wealth of leather bound medical books, gave the impression that our Mr Baker spent every second year on refresher courses.

He didn't waste any further words before giving Minty a thorough examination.

"It's difficult to tell....maybe not the most severe case....definitely mongol, of course."

Of course, of course, of course! But why 'of course'? As if ninety-nine babies out of a hundred were mongol. What right had he to be so complacent in his acceptance?

"With patience, with inestimable patience, and an equal degree of understanding, you will make her socially acceptable." And after such a body blow, he added deprecatingly, "And they are very loving you know."

It was as if by going from the particular to the general, a disaster could somehow be treated light-heartedly. Love suddenly became a very cheap commodity: something to fall back on when all other qualities absented themselves. He spent some further time observing.

Twice he repeated, "No, I really don't think she is the most severe case." And I thought 'Not quite like Jimmy McMahon then; not quite'.

He did pretty much what Doctor Cruickshank had done the night he had given us the news in his surgery, and I felt we were reliving a nightmare.

"You must accept that she will remain a baby for a long time. In fact, your daughter will take longer to pass through every stage of her development than an ordinary child. That's all mongolism is really. Just a slowing down of all the processes. Growth, reactions, mental and physical development. Though of course, there will come an end to her development; she will not attain adulthood in the way of normal people. She will retain childlike qualities throughout her life."

He chose his words with care. Qualities rather than 'characteristics'.

"Try never to compare her with a child of similar age. That would not be fair either to her or to yourselves. Let her proceed and develop at her own speed - and sometimes there won't appear to be any speed or development at all, but be patient. Push very gently when you feel that in normal circumstances you would have persuaded another child to reach for the next stage, but never insist on reaching a goal, or you will only find yourselves in a panic situation. Much of what a normal child achieves *will* happen, but much more slowly."

I knew that both of us were feeling that we hadn't yet got the answer we had come all this way for; the answer Doc Cruickshank was unable to give us.

"Is she....will she be..?" This was evidently not the first time he had been asked the question.

"She will be more than a vegetable. She will have a character of her own. A relationship between you *will* be possible. But much of it will be up to you and the time you can give her. And if you can't bear it, remember there are alternatives. There are some extremely good Care Homes"

His nurse showed us out, making an unintentionally obvious effort not to be patronising, but because all her working hours were spent in dealing with situations similar to ours, it was impossible for her to be anything more than professional, albeit with sympathetic performance. For confirming Doc Cruickshank's grave summation, Mr Baker would send the bill in due course.

"Socially acceptable. Isn't that what the elite want of their daughters when they send them off to finishing school?"

"I think 'socially desirable' is actually the term used, honey," returned Bob as we descended the steps to the sidewalk. "You wait, little old Minty will knock 'em all into a cocked hat!"

I jerked my head to look at his face; he looked genuinely happy. I noted this remark as being significant of his first attempt at optimism. It was infectious and I began to catch his spirit. My step was consciously lighter, and for the first time in my life I knew beyond doubt what it meant to be grateful for small mercies. Minty, however backward, was *not* a vegetable. Some degree of attainment awaited her, and us. One day, she would walk, and talk. Not soon, but certainly one day!

Two weeks ago, the degree of retardation didn't matter; to be retarded at all was a tragedy. Now it somehow meant so much, that she was not a severe case. There was the world's difference between severity and 'certainly mongol, of course'. I had no conception whether Jimmy McMahon was considered severe. I personally could not contemplate anything more so, but if I had gained any wisdom at all in the past weeks, it was that one could be taken completely unawares by pain, but that ultimately it was not the degree of hurt so much as one's ability to accept it that was the important issue. In those few moments after leaving the consulting room, each of us began just a little, to learn to accept.

Snug in her snowsuit, and encircled by Bob's arms, Minty was blissfully and somnolently unaware that she had a single problem. We had been so consumed by the dilemma she presented to us, it had not occurred to us that the biggest problem of all would one day be hers. Bob hugged her more closely, shielding her face from the easterly wind, and I slipped my arm through his. At that moment I felt the loving joy of motherhood for probably the first time. It would be all right.....somehow. Whatever else she was not, Minty was ours, just ours, and ridiculous as it seemed in the face of all the evidence, she was to me the most beautiful little thing this side of heaven.

"Bob, could we go and buy her a teddy or something?"

"Sure. Come on, let's give Santa Claus a hand."

And so it was that an hour later, with steps that could fairly be described as jaunty, and laden with soft toys, we began to search out the restaurant where Arnold and Jill would be waiting, in the centre of London.

There were not many such restaurants in the Canada I had so far discovered, and I warmed to dear old abrasive Arnold who had demonstrated a sensitivity few associated with him in seeking out somewhere that could almost have been part of a Suffolk village. They waved as we entered and were visibly relieved that we were not tense and anxious. Walking directly to the table they had reserved, a waiter took us by surprise as he tapped Bob's shoulder.

"I'm very sorry Sir, but we don't normally allow children in this part of the restaurant."

His use of the word normally suggested there were exceptions, so I intervened.

"Oh please, our friends have reserved a table, and we've no-one with whom to leave her. We're visitors in town, and it was essential she came with us."

The waiter glanced in the direction of the manager who was standing within earshot. He looked at our sleeping daughter.

"I wish I could relax like that! We'll make an exception on this occasion, Sir, but I must ask you to leave if she disturbs the other guests."

"She won't squawk

Bob was tight-lipped in his assurance, so much so that it seemed to jolt the waiter into leading us straight to Jill and Arnold who had obviously said they were awaiting us. He relieved us of our coats and our purchases, and I observed Jill's pleasure that we had not felt too distraught to fit in some shopping.

"And I thought *we'd* bought out the whole of London," Arnold joked. "Looks as if one of us will be travelling back on the roof!"

"Reckon that can be old Teddy, then," Bob rubbed his hands together appreciatively. "Gee that food looks good."

In any other circumstances, Arnold's natural curiosity would have been unrestrained, but today it was unfair to wait to be asked how we had fared.

"We had some tremendous news," Bob began and eyebrows lifted in delight, if also surprise, and then fell again as he continued, "Minty is not as bad as we feared."

Because we were pleased, so they were too, but even in their genuine pleasure they could not disguise the fact that they were perplexed that we should be so thrilled about Minty not being so severely handicapped. They were at the stage we had somehow, in the course of this day, passed through. Retardation of any kind was a disaster. At least they wouldn't have to resort to discussing topics they had obviously prepared should they have needed to take our minds off the reason for our visit to London.

They relaxed completely, and Arnold prepared to do justice to the menu, but not before he declared, "With my characteristic lack of tact, and because I know you two will forgive me, I want to tell you our news."

Bob was all attention as Jill began to admonish him. "Oh Arnold, you agreed not now..."

I squeezed Jill's arm to tell her it didn't matter. We had had all the attention for two weeks now, and besides, I guessed I wasn't going to be totally surprised. Jill's anxiety at Minty's retardation had been rather deeper than one would usually have expected of an outsider. Before Arnold could say another word, and almost as if my gesture had given her permission to be happy, she said quietly. "Yes, if you haven't already cottoned on, we are going to have a baby too."

We toasted the unborn baby, we toasted Minty, we toasted ourselves, and suddenly Bob and I were hurdling again. The world had not stopped. Life would go on.

"You'll be godparents of course," pronounced Arnold. Wouldn't dream of anyone else." And that really did put us on the spot. Jill shook her head unable to believe her ears.

"Oh sorry Jill, I know we should have discussed it," he apologised completely missing the point. "I just assumed you'd want Bob and Helen."

"And so I do," she began, and Bob came to the rescue.

"In the circumstances we'll delay the choice of godparents for Minty, Arnold. It would be a lot to take on board for anyone who considered it seriously."

"Sorry folks. No wonder Jill despairs of me." Arnold, direct as always, continued. "I feel a heel, but I don't think I could...

"Thanks for saying it fella," Bob bit hard again. "Most people would have made an excuse. Of course, we would never have asked you. But only you could have goofed that one. Strangely enough, you've just pushed us over our first hurdle - coping with other people's reactions. It was like an injection; a brief initial pain, and after that there can only be increased strength. So thanks pal. And I really mean that."

The two men exchanged slaps on the back, argued about who should pay the bill and went off to the gents, all of which gave Jill and me the chance to exchange a few hitherto unspoken thoughts.

"It won't happen to you as well," I assured her, "so put the thought right out of your mind."

"I'm sorry if the fear showed," she apologised characteristically. "I wouldn't have done that for the world."

"It would be unavoidable: an involuntary reaction. I was the same about Jimmy McMahon." I told her all about the incident, how though I felt ashamed, I could do nothing to repair matters.

"You mean like Arnold saying he couldn't be godfather to Minty?"

I had not in fact thought of it like that at all, but now Arnold's reaction made me feel human. His refusal hadn't meant he wanted nothing to do with us, just that at that moment he did not feel he could cope with the demands. Perhaps, similarly, Mrs McMahon would not write me off; may even accept an apology.

"Jill, do one thing for me. If at any time you feel that you can't come and see us because of Minty...not just now...but later when she's older, promise to give me the real reason...not just make excuses."

Jill laughed aloud which was something new for her, and she continued to laugh. "You really think there's any doubt about telling you straight out, with a husband like Arnold around?"

"Thank God for Arnold then!" I shared her amusement.

"So what are you two finding so hilarious?" was Arnold's immediate question as the men reappeared.

"You, replied his wife. "And we are not going to explain."

CHAPTER FIVE

The drive back was memorable, not only because it was so breathtakingly beautiful but because we were travelling the same road we had travelled twelve hours ago feeling so negative, beaten and hopeless. Now in a new positive mood Jill and Arnold could talk openly about *their* child without getting a complex about hurting us; we could look forward to Christmas, to a future. Not quite the one we were expecting, but a future all the same. And who knew what it would bring?

The moon shone out clear and cold on the highway, and as we neared home, the deer on the roadside grew more numerous, the 'bush' on either side, denser. There was a growing feeling of limitless space; 'a serene, wild land where a man could breathe' was how Doc Cruickshank described it. And all the time Minty slept and smiled, and I knew at last that I loved her; knew too that had the verdict been worse, it would have made no difference. Tomorrow we'd go out, Bob and I, a little way into the bush and choose a Christmas tree; a freedom and luxury that would have been inconceivable in England. Families would be out with their sleighs ready to pull home the chosen trees, and the ones they took away would make no impression on the thousands that were left clustered into the vast expanse of bush.

Despite the almost frightening wilderness, there was sheer regal beauty pervading this part of Canada; the lush spruce and firs thrust determinedly straight, and before they could grow old and weary, were felled to become the structure of a hunter's cabin, or weekend retreat. Because of its very nature, the land commanded respect, and in return it yielded of its beauty and gifts. No license needed here to fish in the lakes or shoot in the bush. Bob and I often took the boat onto the lake with the roughest of nets and within seconds of lowering them, we would secure a catch. It was so pleasurably easy and finding it so, the community had an unwritten rule that one took home the fish that were needed, returning those that were superfluous, to the lake.

We had chosen this wild and free land, where youngsters could skate, ski, and play ice hockey in winter, and sail, swim, ride and fish in summer without wandering from their own doorsteps. Not that we didn't fish in winter - a hole in the ice, a stool and anorak were all that were required, but in summer it was such a deliriously lazy and rewarding exercise. This was where we had intended to bring up our family - three, or maybe four, healthy offspring.

And now little Minty had brought all this to a full stop. What need had *she* of frozen lakes or skis? What joy would *she* derive from canoeing over still silent lakes as the sun was setting, and looking ahead to the twinkling lights of a log cabin? Would *she* ever ask for a baseball bat for her birthday? Would she even know it was her birthday? And of course, there would be no other children now. We couldn't possibly take the risk. Somehow Bob and I had agreed on that without a word having been spoken. Minty would be our family; not the one we had planned, but her condition would not permit the addition of other children. These were my undisclosed thoughts. It never occurred to me that Bob was not entirely in tune.

Later events were to prove to us that we were not God!

The day did eventually come when I was able to greet Doc Cruickshank with a 'Good-morning' that did not contain thoughts like 'You are the man who told me she was backward' thrown in between the two words. He himself of course did not fail to notice the easing of tension and one day as we passed, he put out his hand and joked, "Tell ye what....I'll give ye fifty dollars for her."

"Make it fifty thousand and you'd still be wasting your time," I said, suddenly amazing myself. "And that reminds me, we haven't yet paid you for bringing her into the world. I'll mention it to Bob tonight."

"Forget it," he replied abruptly, and we both stopped, because now it wasn't just a remark in passing.

"It wasn't your fault," I stammered. And then, "Was it?" I was aware that my expression was half-questioning, half accusing. "I mean nothing happened while she was being delivered did it?"

And now he looked less tense, as if my question had relieved him of an associated guilt, which albeit irrational, he had nonetheless felt.

"No, brain damage occurs sometimes during delivery, but mongolism is decided at the moment of conception. But there will be time enough for us to discuss the how, why and when. Whether or not a baby's handicap has anything to do with the doctor who delivered her, has little bearing on the emotion he has when telling the parents, and for a while he shares the responsibility they themselves insist on bearing."

His comment brought us very close.

"We're as pleased with the goods you delivered as any other Ma and Pa," I insisted. "And thank you."

He smiled ruefully. "I can recall a certain evening in the not so distant past when you weren't exactly the satisfied customer. That was a hell of a night," he added barely audibly.

"But that's behind us now." I wasn't sure whether I believed my own words or was still in the process of trying to convince myself.

"But there are still some things that aren't?" he asked.

"Too many."

"Give it time. Time's a great healer. Aye gie it time."

Is that all it needs? I wondered. Time might indeed heal, but how much could it change? In time, everyone would know Minty was mongol. In time they would be able to talk to me about her, and I to

42

them, with an absence of embarrassment. In time Minty herself might accomplish some of those things that other people's babies did as a matter of course. But time, for all its powers would not change Minty into a normal little girl. I repeated, but this time aloud, "Is time all it needs?"

"No." He hesitated, and chose his words with care. "But time will give you all that *you* need."

I wanted to believe him but all I could do was trust. After all, he hadn't gone through life with his eyes shut, or without gaining experience.

"Tell me." he said, and then added, "Though of course ye mustn't if ye don't want to. Have ye got a religion?"

"Not just now. Not since..." I replied and found difficulty in trying to enlarge. "I rather wish I had. I don't deny the possibility, or dispute the existence of a God. It's just that He is so remote....unreal." Even as I spoke, I knew I had denied the old minister of my childhood church who had encouraged me through my teens into the belief that I could reach university. I hadn't sought out a church in Canada and certainly with the advent of Minty, I would not have wanted to go anywhere near one. What was any God doing to allow such mistakes?

Doc only nodded and with considerable puffing walked to his parked car. Winding down the window, he said, "Drop in whenever ye like."

I thanked him, wondering why he had raised the question of religion. The existence of a God I could no longer be sure of, but knew instinctively that my needs in that respect were being supplied by Doc Cruickshank himself. I could not imagine that he would not forever be in the background. He was my reference, my comforter, and when he saw the need of it, my donor of common sense.

And so it was that Minty, with his constant reassurance entered her sixth month, sitting up in her buggy, helped to a greater or lesser degree - I was too biased to assess accurately - by a small pillow and set of reins. She could pat-a-cake, and wave goodbye, and smile bewitchingly. Gradually we discovered that the world had not stopped spinning because we had given birth to a mentally handicapped child, and as the shock wore off, we began to slip into a routine that closely resembled that of most young couples with a new baby.

CHAPTER SIX

It was one Saturday afternoon, when Bob was repairing the kitchen shelves, that we experienced the first link between us, and other parents in similar circumstances. Actually I think it was the first time we had become aware that there *were* other retarded children in this tiny Canadian town, apart from Jimmy McMahon of course.

Carol had collected our mail whilst out shopping and had given the letters to Bob when he went out to the garden shed for nails.

"Anything from England?"

"No, but one with a local postmark."

I wondered who lived far enough away from us in this tiny community, to bother writing. Folks usually preferred to drop in, or call informally on the telephone, especially as local phone calls were free of charge.

"Probably a reminder to pay a bill." Tossing a couple of circulars on the table, Bob slit the envelope open to reveal it was from the Mentally Handicapped Association.

"There surely aren't enough to form an Association," he reflected. And then added, "Though I suppose even a handful, with two parents and four grandparents each, would make a sizeable group. Maybe we should add our support."

"Maybe." I was unconvinced.

"Helen whether or not we take out a formal membership, we have been part of that group from the day Minty was born."

I could imagine them all telling us how to face up to things, how soon we'd be able to accept it.....could see them now...middle aged, elegant ladies with time to spare for those less fortunate.

"Haven't you noticed, no-one who actually *has* a child like Minty has been near us yet? They, at least, know that we have needed time, not words of condolence to sort it all out." And then I remembered Mrs McMahon and how I'd given her short shrift. I had not told Bob about the encounter because I didn't want to tell him of the unforgivable way I had behaved. But I did now; I told him how she hadn't interfered, or lectured, or been offended by my response to her overtures. She hadn't even revealed how hurt she must have been at my reaction to Jimmy.

"I'm sorry Bob; I'm just cynical and unreasonable...yes we must go...but together, eh?"

"How else, you nut?"

"By the way," I said, "I don't pass Jimmy by now without waving. You know he sits in the doorway of his parents hardware store."

"Great gal," Bob smiled. "Glad you've told me. I'll look out for him myself from now on."

Looking out for Jimmy, and waving to him, was in fact, now an essential part of each shopping excursion, which incidentally I still undertook in the early evening. But I knew too that I always found some reason to be walking on the opposite side of the street when I passed. Physical contact was something I could not yet contemplate. Self-examination would begin some ten yards before the store. 'How would you feel if people spurned Minty this way? Go on speak to him...shake his hand...'

'Minty isn't the same.'

'She has to be...'

'No, not my baby. Not my girl.'

And so it would last until we were well clear of the store.

On one occasion I had asked an acquaintance how old Jimmy was, and stupidly had failed to prepare myself for her answer.

"He must be twenty-four or five, I guess."

I had endeavoured to give the impression of flippancy, as if her reply didn't really matter one way or the other.

"But he still plays," I began, and then checked myself, but not before I had let her see that her answer had had the effect of a death sentence.

"Well, of course he does. I mean he's mentally retarded -everyone knows. But why should it matter to you Helen?" I expect the fact that I blanched gave it away. She stared at me in disbelief. "Oh! You don't mean..."

The world had to know sometime. I didn't go home, but walked in the direction of the surgery.

"Is Dr Cruickshank busy?" I enquired of his nurse.

"Well surgery hasn't actually begun yet. Would you like me to make an appointment for you?" she offered.

"No, not really. It isn't imperative I see him today. In fact it was stupid of me to bother. It's just that he said to call whenever I needed to."

"Well then, that's exactly what you've done. Is it Suzie? Perhaps I can help if it's nothing serious."

"No, no actually it's Jimmy McMahon."

Her eyebrows raised, and only her impeccable manners prevented her from asking what Jimmy McMahon had to do with me.

"Could you please tell me - is he really in his twenties?"

She came round to my side of the dispensary hatch on the pretext of arranging the magazines and simultaneously, and psychologically, removed the professional barrier between us.

"I guess you've already been told that you must never compare Suzie with normal children and their achievements, otherwise you are likely to make yourself, and her very miserable and frustrated."

I nodded. "Dr Cruickshank and the specialist mentioned it."

"Pity neither of them thought to tell you not to compare mongol with mongol, also," she commented forthrightly. "For there's almost the same extreme range of ability within their group as in the normal strata. Now just because Jimmy is still playing with soldiers at twenty-five doesn't mean Suzie will be."

"Forgive me," I said apologetically, "but someone must have tried to console Jimmy's mother in this way too."

"Sure," she replied looking at me directly, and accepting my challenge, "Doc Cruickshank's old father did, just before he died."
I had not expected to hear her say this, and registered surprise.

"Then why...? I mean Jimmy *is* playing with soldiers at twenty-five, despite all the assurance."

"Oh make no mistake. Jimmy's mother didn't come here seeking an assurance that her boy wouldn't be playing with soldiers in his twenties. She had seen an adolescent mongol who was still pushed around in a buggy, and was incontinent. So believe me, she's mighty pleased Jim enjoys his toys for she was able to give his buggy away years ago."

Nurse Timson continued to look me straight in the eye, compassion in her gentle smile. "It doesn't pay to look too far ahead you know. Try to enjoy the present...the present being that you have a daughter who is very much like any other baby, soft and warm, and adorably cuddly, and whose smile could melt the heart of a Scrooge." She tickled Minty's chin and received a delighted raspberry in return.

"You know," she said, feigning a philosophical air, "I don't believe she has as many complaints about the world as you seem to think she ought to have."
The tension of an hour ago began to filter away, and the sound of Doc Cruickshank's car could be heard on the driveway.

"I'll be off," I said, "and thanks for the chat."

"No, it's I who should be thanking you; you've sure polished my halo tonight." And as I was going out of the door she added, "By the way, you may not believe it, but I envy you." Ignoring my amazed expression, she went on, "You might drop by again and share her with me. Selfish creatures that we are, loneliness sometimes appears a greater problem than retardation."

She was absolutely serious. My first instinct was to invite her over but she might interpret this as sympathy so instead I asked her why lonely people often gave the impression they didn't need other folk.

"Just a cover up - a feeling that one has to give the impression one's choice was exactly what nature or circumstances had dictated anyway. And I'll accept that very kind invitation you were about to offer me when you stopped yourself in case I'd think you were feeling sorry I'd been left on the shelf - isn't that what you say in England?"

The barriers had all come crashing down and we were just two personalities in accord.

The snow blew into my face as we walked home, but did nothing to lessen the warmth that accompanied the discovery of a new friend. Halting momentarily I said aloud, "Minty, I didn't make that friend; you did! You knocked my good old English reserve for six!"

I determined that tomorrow I would go and see Jimmy McMahon. If all I had now read about mongol children were true, he would probably touch me. There would be other youngsters too in the little old schoolhouse that had been made available to them and where Jimmy, I now knew, spent two days each week; over-affectionate children who would feel Minty's soft face, and want us to sit down and play.

And I almost made it. Rachel Timson had introduced a different slant on Minty's retardation, and I awoke with what I thought was a new confidence. But if Bob had noticed it, he had chosen not to comment, so immediately after seeing him off to the High School and clearing away the breakfast dishes, I zipped up Minty in her snowsuit. The rest of the chores could wait - best to go whilst courage was running high. I set out briskly, keenly appreciating the biting freshness of the winter morning realising that I hadn't noticed the weather for weeks. Not that the Canadian climate held as much variety or lack of predictability as the English. Once winter set in come October, it was here to stay until the end of March. Spring, like autumn, was a brief two weeks of glorious change, and in summer one could plan picnics and days at the cabin quite confident that whatever else spoilt one's plans, it certainly would not be the weather.

In Red Lake we had noted, and commented on, the temperature, as often as the English commented on the changeability of their weather. 'Ten below' was not a rarity, and in the depth of winter much lower temperatures were recorded.

I determined to shake off the lethargy and bitterness of past weeks and for the first time began to feel able to tackle the problems that had enveloped us like a rough heavy blanket every waking hour. The wooden houses grew fewer, and the road rougher and less clearly defined as we approached the 'schoolhouse' where a certain Mrs Huss organised a sheltered workshop cum play centre for the mentally and physically handicapped.

The small building stood warmly red-brown against its stark snow-drenched background. I could hear a gramophone record being played and a variety of voices accompanying it. The creased red face of Mrs Huss beckoned to me from the window, and I halted the buggy under the shelter of the eaves.

"Come in and welcome," she called. "You're just in time for coffee. Bring the baby in - we're all longing to see her."

The little world inside promised warmth and reassurance. Holding Minty in my left arm - a cumbersome bundle in her snowsuit - I struggled to close the heavy door with my right, and then turned to greet the occupants. As I did so my legs grew weak beneath me. My expression, I knew, was registering sheer horror at the row of round, deadpan faces in front of me. I willed my facial muscles to smile; they certainly weren't helping me to speak. And then there was a long silence.

Eyes wandered from me to Minty. Someone's finger pointed, but the action was undefined, and the arm seemed to lose track of whether it was intended to go up or down. I think Mrs Huss was saying something, but though hearing the voice, I did not comprehend the words. Tongues. Huge, lolling ugly tongues; my eyes, though repulsed, could not leave them. I felt trapped, and panicked. My fingers gripped Minty's suit. I do not know how long I took to say it; only that nausea forced me to seek the door handle. "I'm so sorry, I have to go. I just remembered something. Sorry. Goodbye."

Once outside, I leaned heavily on the door that I had so unforgivably closed. Fresh air swarmed into my lungs, and I gasped it gratefully. I do not recall ever in my life feeling so desperately lonely. When, eventually, we reached home, the retching of my body exhausted me into fitful sleep. Some time later, the phone rang and my need for it to be Bob on the end of the line made it impossible for me to contemplate it being anyone else. Stumbling, I grabbed at the receiver. "Bob, it was terrible. I can't possibly take her there again. We've got to make her normal. We must. She isn't going to be one of them. I couldn't bear it. We..." Any further words gave way to the choking sobbing I had stifled on the journey home.

"It is very hard in the beginning Mrs Wade." My grip on the receiver slackened as the voice that was not Bob's met my ear.

"Who are you?"

"I'm calling from the school. You came to see me this morning, but unfortunately you had to leave rather hurriedly."

"Yes, yes I did." I made no attempt at an apology for none would be adequate. I had so unjustifiably, insulted both her, and her school by slamming the door this morning, and now I had informed her what a dreadful place she ran. Why hadn't she put the phone down? Why was she still calm, so kind, still waiting?

"I wonder Mrs Wade, if you would like to give us a second chance? We tend not to be at our best in a new situation, even if the new situation is only being introduced to someone."

"I wasn't exactly at my best either," I whispered; a comment she chose to ignore.

"They will probably be equally confused the next time you come too," she warned, suddenly dropping the royal 'we', "and no more prepossessing. Anyway, think it over, and drop by when you think you can stand them."

"Oh but..." But she had hung up

I was confused. Her words were those one would use to describe people one abhorred, and yet I knew of the deep affection she had for those youngsters; obviously a tremendously practical affection that faced up to the truth, and withstood the warts and all.

The sheer wretchedness of the day hung heavily and drained me of even shame and ineptitude. Lethargically I existed until I heard Bob's footsteps nearing the back door.

"Hello love. How was it?"

I looked at him slowly as if to ascertain that this time I really was talking to my husband. With no definite emotion I said, "You have a bitch of a wife." And through supper I recounted the morning's events.

"I shouldn't have let you go when I saw how you were this morning," he chided himself, his head cupped in his hands.

I was perplexed. "I don't understand."

"Oh all that buoyancy and confidence. It was so obviously an act; you were going to crack at the least provocation."

To no avail I endeavoured to assure him that I really was feeling better and that I had been convinced it was the perfect day to make the visit.

"Um...until you actually got there. How many were there?"

"I don't know: I didn't give myself time to notice anything."

"It seems to me you noticed a whole lot - certainly enough to make you run away. I should have been with you."

"Don't make excuses for me, Bob."

We each recoiled into a very private and lonely world, into the security of companionable silence, reluctant to inflict the inevitable pain that discussion, however gently conducted, would cause us both. Despite the cliché 'It's not what you say; it's the way that you say it'; it was for us the subject that yielded the pain, no matter how expressed.

The necessity of returning hung over me like an unpleasant chore, and in a desperate attempt to rid it of personal significance, I added it to my daily list of jobs to be done, along with 'collect dry cleaning' and 'make dental appointment'. Bob didn't mention it for over two weeks, but there were always gaps in our conversation, and in the silence I could hear him asking me about it as surely as if he were shouting the words. When sufficient silence had passed for the topic to have been raised, we would resume the conversation, unjustifiably feeling cleaner for having disposed of an unpleasant task.

He was fixing a burst pipe one morning - I was plumber's mate - when he said in a tone that was intended to be casual but which was as a result of the effort, distinctly brittle, "Tell you what - I'll give you a hand with the mess, and then we'll both go."

"Go where?"

The question was superfluous. "You're right; I have to go back. But Mrs Huss has a low enough opinion of me without my taking you along to hold my hand."

"Nonsense. I'm Minty's poppa. What better reason?"

"Maybe, but folks tend to get all formal when a deputation arrives. Why don't you just collect us?"

I expected difficulty in convincing him that this was a visit I just had to make on my own, if only to offset to some slight degree the offence I must have caused on my first call. I was therefore shaken when he replied, "That's a good idea. Yes, why not?"

He had spoken hurriedly. I followed him into the garage to where his greasy capable hands putting away the tools. Those greasy capable hands were shaking. So he hated the idea as much as I did.

"Oh Bob, why didn't you say?"

"And where would that have got us? We'd have commiserated and never gone near the place!"

And so it was that we indulged ourselves by not being stoical, and the visit was again postponed. But we conceded that one day Minty *would* be a pupil and that we would attend all her school functions as readily as if she were normal. But not today. Rushing at life's problems would not remove them, nor yet increase our strength to take them on board.

Some weeks later I did return. No special day, and for no special reason other than that *not* going had gone on for long enough. I committed myself by phone before I left, to prevent any risk of turning back.

"Oh how wonderful," Mrs. Huss enthused, "my assistant is away today, and I'd so much appreciate your help."

"I really can't imagine what use I could possibly be after the way I behaved last time."

"You can tie some shoe laces at playtime - it always takes ages...and that's a job that doesn't require you to look at the children themselves."

For a brief second her comment offended me until I accepted that I deserved to be insulted. And, of course, she wasn't being offensive, just utterly down to earth. Practical - matter of fact.

"I deserve your poor opinion of me."

"Not at all. It's better to be honest. And, of course, it helps to make the day you find you neither notice nor care that they are different, so much more wonderful. See you shortly!"

I didn't believe that that day would ever come for me, but I chose not to take the bait and promised to be there in fifteen minutes.

Back on the doorstep, humble and unprepared, my first knock was so feeble even I didn't hear it. My knuckles were in the process of a second attempt when the door was opened. Out of the corner of my eye I observed Mrs Huss' assistant leaving by a side exit. I was obviously being manoeuvred and only momentarily resented this gentle push into the deep end.

"Reporting for duty," I attempted a smile, simultaneously keeping my gaze away from the occupants. In seconds I learned that 'keeping one's distance' is alien to mongol children. They snapped up my physical presence as eagerly as bright children lap up a story. Someone grasped my wrist; another had his arm around my waist.

"Baby, see baby."

I pulled Minty's shawl away from her face, and when she smiled there was spontaneous appreciation and delight.

But I was totally unprepared when a boy of about eleven snatched her from me. Like a flash Mrs Huss flung herself heavily in front of him.

"Wayne!" Returning Minty to my arms she grasped the boy firmly by the shoulders, remonstrating in short sharp phrases. The other children were genuinely distressed. In the years that followed I was to learn most forcibly that mongol children always behave genuinely. Wayne's head hung in disgrace and unreserved repentance.

"Please hug him," Mrs Huss almost pleaded. "He was so jealous of your obvious love for the baby."

"Oh but..."

"Please" she insisted, and I was as a child under her jurisdiction. I put my arm around the lad who beamed in response and his face was a strange mixture of tears and delight.

"You lu me" he mouthed jerkily, unable to cope with end consonants.

"Yes," I lied, "and the baby loves you too. Look she's smiling again."

"Speak slowly to him," came a quiet voice from behind. "Very slowly." I bent lower and his dribble oozed onto my collar, and again, as I knew I would, I longed to escape the suddenly nauseating, stifling room.

"You um morrow. Baby um morrow?"

"We'll come tomorrow to see Wayne," I heard myself promising in a hoarse whisper. He nodded vigorously, and then gradually slackened his grip and lumbered back to his chair.

Uncomprehending, the rest of the children had silently witnessed the scene, and with the gentlest gestures had demonstrated their sorrow that this should have happened. Lacking eloquence, they had nevertheless communicated precisely their feelings, as indeed they communicated their total forgiveness of Wayne, whom they seemed instinctively to know, couldn't help himself.

During the course of the morning I learned that Wayne was not eleven, but seventeen. And each day he was reminded that his parents had still not come to terms with his condition. On their way to church or the homes of friends, they would drop him off at Grandpa's - the only person who had time for him outside of school. He was not mongol and had none of the associated characteristics. Severely retarded, and with a strong tendency towards sullenness, his refusal to co-operate was emphasised by the diametrically opposed personalities of the mongols whose sheer delight it was to please those whose charges they were.

"Wayne - show Mrs Wade how well you read."

"Read!" I could not conceal the amazement in my voice.

"I can see we have some surprises in store for you," Mrs Huss beamed. But Wayne made no attempt to produce his reading book. Instead he stared fixedly at Minty, and I feared a repetition of his jealousy.

"Me read baby," he stammered fiercely, producing his reader from inside his jersey. But when I invited him to begin, he did not respond and his hand remained limply over the print. He continued to gaze at Minty, and she, as if comprehending the situation in its entirety, smiled the most genuine smile, and what he construed to be her delight in his attention, evoked three laborious phrases. His pleasure at my spontaneous applause was obvious, and then for no apparent reason, he wept uncontrollably.

I was bewildered that a human being so lacking in mental capacity could suffer emotionally to such a degree. So simple a mind; so complex a problem. He understood his rejection as acutely as if he had checked its meaning in a dictionary. Financially he appeared to be indulged: an expensive wristwatch, and expertly cut trousers. Enough perhaps, to alleviate their consciences about the time his parents did *not* give him? Who was I to judge? Might I also face a long lonely struggle towards acceptance?

Eager, clumsy hands demanded I look at sewing, painting and plasticine models. Only the large placid form of Jimmy McMahon at the corner table made no attempt to attract my attention. He was persevering with unlimited patience, to complete a boot scraper, made from a rubber mat and beer bottle tops. I was certain he was not unaware of my presence, merely ignoring it - though not rudely. I was to experience this many times with Minty as she grew older. Once rebuffed she did not place herself in a position of vulnerability again.

"Hello Jimmy," I ventured, for the surprising reason that I cared that he was being so aloof. "I like your mat."

With apparent indifference that was immediately contradicted by his subsequent action, he fixed the last bottle cap in place, and lifted the mat towards my face.

"For baby. You take home."

The mat itself was valueless; the accomplishment it signified, beyond price, and I felt as embarrassed as if accepting the Crown Jewels from a high-ranking Royal. He still did not smile, but placed the mat firmly in the buggy.

"You have."

"I just couldn't...." I implored Mrs Huss to intervene. She grinned at my predicament.

"What inhibitions civilised society inflicts upon conditioned adults!" She raised her hands in mock horror. "Jimmy McMahon wishes to present Mrs Wade with a boot scraper, but Mrs Wade feels she cannot possibly accept! Possibly because she has no gift in exchange?"

"No it's not that," I insisted, unable to obliterate my unforgivable reaction to Jimmy when I had encountered him with his mother that evening.

"So, it must be for some equally normal and stupid reason! Go on give Jimmy a lot of pleasure and take it! You know they may be the proverbial lilies of the field, but completely unwittingly they must surely be some of the shrewdest investors in human emotion!"

I began to relax somewhat, and to take in the surroundings. There were eight youngsters in the bungalow-school which consisted of a large rectangular room in which the lightweight furniture could be moved to suit the needs of the occupants, a smaller but more robustly equipped room for handwork, sewing and cooking, a large storage area which divided this from the bathroom and a teacher's study whose main purpose appeared to be to house an expensive radiogram and generous record collection. This was the only area to be out of bounds.

A smiling, agreeable five year old was the baby of the group, whilst Jimmy was the eldest. Ability was in no apparent way commensurate with age, and Wayne, when co-operative, showed signs of being mentally the most capable, whilst Ruth, a frail scrap of a girl, a close second. At nine she wrote much as a normal five to six year old; with large uncertain figures she revealed a mastery of simple arithmetic.

She was apparently something of an enigma being unable to reproduce a single written word learned some days previously, whilst verbally repeating a story she had heard only once, presented her with no challenge. She was not mongol, but had long since failed to compete with her peers and had thus been referred to this minute, sheltered school where she became so much more relaxed and happy and forthcoming.

Another girl was clumsily but conscientiously endeavouring to sew a cross-stitch pattern around the border of a tray cloth. Just as long as someone was available at the relevant moment to thread her needle or to put a knot in a new length of thread, all was well, but if not, she merely continued without those facilities, working on such a decreased length of silk that her work became so bunched it was impossible to pass a needle through any part of it. But for the fact that her small body was beginning to show signs of adolescence, I would have judged her to be seven or eight. She was, in fact, fifteen.

The curled hair, achieved by an over-zealous amateur hairdresser, could not disguise her condition. Gently in the extreme, she stroked my arm whenever I passed. She introduced me to her friend by pointing a finger and smiling in the direction of another, considerably more retarded girl who was holding a doll in the very same way I was supporting Minty, who was cradled in my left arm but resting slightly on my hip. As I changed her position for comfort, so Emily moved her doll. She had positioned the doll's pram beside Minty's buggy, and I now noticed that one of the blankets had been transferred!

I went to sit beside her but there was no hint that my presence was welcome or otherwise. I was acutely aware of my inadequacy, simultaneously making small talk despite the fact that she understood little or nothing of what I was saying. Later that year I came to realize the value of being able to drop down to, and to remain in first gear without becoming frustrated at achieving so little. But on this first occasion, I was awkward and constantly looked about me to decide where next to plant myself. And the observant Mrs Huss, it was apparent, missed nothing.

Returning to Emily, I abandoned efforts to chat, as she silently stroked Minty's arm

"You are giving her the thing she loves most," Mrs Huss said from behind the pasting table. "With Emily you need to do no more than to be beside her. After you've gone your visit will be mirrored in all she does. She will imitate your mannerisms for the rest of the day."

It was flattering to think I had actually displayed any mannerisms for I had felt myself to be so colourless and lacklustre whilst here. How little was required to give Emily and those who shared her world, so much pleasure. I reflected on the incredible range of man's intellect. There were those who would strive to fathom the secrets of the universe in their quest for mental satisfaction, and others, like Emily, whose ultimate contentment would result from the mere presence of another human being, and with whom no words need be spoken. Someone whose name would matter little and what she said even less.

Mrs Huss began to help two children to clear away their things and I took my cue.

"Shall I help you to clear up," I asked Jimmy hesitantly.

Immediately a whisper from behind. "Not a question - that implies a choice, which is difficult. Just tell him clearly what to do." There was no reaction to my instruction, and assuming my directness had offended him, I sought to rephrase it.

"Not so quick," Mrs Huss laughed. "Give it time to sink in."

"He has understood?"

"Yes, but the response will take time. You'll get used to us!"

I began to help, but she apprehended my movements.

"If you do that, you won't be sure he *has* understood, or whether he is merely copying your actions."

Jimmy's head turned slowly, and as his eyes met mine for the first time, I felt a great surge of sheer pleasure. So he bore no grudge that he would have had every justification in feeling.

"Finish?" His mouth did not close after the question and I waited for more but none came.

"Yes finish. Put your tops away now."

He looked first at me, then at the table strewn with the remaining tops, and then, as if an electric switch inside him had been pressed, he grinned. "Me put way. You help?"

The relief at knowing we had communicated was exhilarating, and we continued at a comparatively hair-raising pace. Once there had been understanding, the tidying up was done meticulously. To my amazement, when the last top had been put into the box, he fetched a cloth and wiped down the table. He watched to see which person I would help next, and walked close behind. A chain reaction ensued, as each one who had been helped joined the ranks of helpers; followed like the Pied Piper. Wayne looked guardedly from the corner of the room, indulging in delaying tactics. With a little contingency in tow, I went over to his table.

"Come on Wayne. Let's see how quickly we can put all these things away."

Even as I said it I realised that 'quickly' was the last word I should have used. Speed had no place in this Peter Pan world, for it only resulted in confusion and insecurity. I must remember that I was not in the normal classroom to which I was accustomed. Albeit subconsciously I suppose I had arrived thinking I knew it all...it would be similar to having a remedial group...

"We'd like to help," I said, starting all over again, and knew instantly that it was no better than the first attempt. Wayne was an extremely jealous child, and I had coupled Jimmy with me in the offer, which only served to put Wayne on the other side of the fence. He put his hands flatly over the raffia he had been weaving, and beyond that he didn't budge...

"I wonder if there will be time for a song after the clearing up is done? Do you think so Wayne?"

"Guess so," he proffered hesitantly. "Baby sing?"

"She doesn't know how to sing yet Wayne. Perhaps you could teach her?"

"She sit with me?"

"I'll put her buggy next to you," I agreed, making doubly certain that her reins were secure.

Instantly the raffia, scissors and cardboard were replaced in the cupboard. He was smiling, and because Wayne was smiling, big Jimmy smiled.

I was to learn this about Downs people: nothing pleases them more than a resolved, happy situation. The method by which that is achieved is a matter of indifference; the reason for it being so, even less. Only that the group in which they find themselves is in pleasant accord, is of any importance, and they thrill to it.

Jimmy trundled off to get a waste paper basket and cleared up the scraps of paper under the table, and then proceeded to perform the same service for several of the others. It was, I decided, a peculiar little army with whom to throw in my lot, but since fate had decided Minty was to be a member of it, I had no choice. The acceptance of a boot scraper was my induction.

Eventually, the orderliness of the room put my lounge to shame. Chairs, with Minty's buggy included, were arranged in a semi circle, and their enjoyment when Mrs Huss put on a record, was boundless. I had not imagined, with all their limitations, that they could throw themselves into anything with so much enthusiasm. But music was the key that unlocked another world, and they swayed, beat time, and tapped their feet to its rhythm.

Most did not resist the hypnotic call of the tune to get up and dance ...alone... with a partner or in a delighted little cluster. And all the time, Wayne sang lustily, gazing intently at Minty in an effort to get her to copy him. When she finally gurgled he was beside himself with joy. "Baby sing...she sing with me!"

I pondered his reaction deeply. I must learn from this child and be satisfied with short advances, even if occasionally I allowed myself the luxury of deceiving myself a little. As long as we were moving ahead at all, at whatever speed, I must not make us all miserable by pressing for more.

And so the afternoon, which in itself had been an education for me, drew to a close. Twenty minutes were allowed for the young folks to put on their coats and outdoor boots.

"Will a bus come to collect them?" I asked.

"Not from this point. Those whose parents don't actually pick them up from school walk along to the next block and wait for the High School bus."

"Alone?"

"Why not?" Mrs Huss was obviously delighted by my surprise. "You'd have no objection to a six or seven year old walking along such a quiet road. Nor would you doubt his ability to stop at an appointed place. Why then shouldn't older people with a mental age of seven do the same?"

Looking back it strikes me what an innocent world we all enjoyed those many years ago. Nowadays, irrespective of a child's intelligence, few of us would be happy for our children to walk down a quiet road unaccompanied, and certainly not for reasons involving his ability to wait at a bus stop. But because it *was* such an innocent world then, I merely asked, if she were not afraid of accidents.

"Life involves risks for us all." She was thoughtful. "The first time a parent allows her child to ride his bicycle beyond his own garden, or to go to the shop...exposure to the outside world and its dangers increases the risks to be faced. But cubs must grow into lions with a need for independence. It is nonetheless true for children who take much longer to grow up. They need most desperately to know that you have trust in their ability to stand without you now and then."

I projected myself forward over the coming years, and imagined Minty, school bag over her shoulder, walking independently to this little school. "Do you think she will?" I said aloud, and I did not have to explain.

"It's early days. Take them one at a time; enjoy each one. In giving you Minty, life has relieved you of many of its pressures to keep abreast of the pace we insist on setting for ourselves."

"You make her handicap sound like a gift," I said.
Mrs. Huss only smiled.

As I watched them all preparing to go home, I felt my first real surge of hope that Minty would have any kind of future at all. Walking to school, or waiting for a school bus. These were things that from the moment I knew of her condition, I had automatically dismissed from my mind.

All hooded and buttoned up, this strange collection of pupils began to leave, waving as they neared the door, neither frantically or casually as my normal class had done, but just by raising an arm in a teddy bear gesture, and smiling hesitantly. Many walked towards waiting parents who greeted them as eagerly as if they had been parted for a month. Such intense affection! Others walked in the direction of Frances Street where they were to wait for the old school bus.

"Are the High School children kind to them?" I had to ask the question.

"Human nature is not always kind," Mrs. Huss replied honestly, but in her eyes was a mixture of anger and sadness. "But they have the best in-built defence mechanism in the world," and to my raised eyebrows she continued. "They see only the good in people and by nature turn the other cheek....makes them almost invulnerable. Hostility cannot continue without retaliation. And after a while those who think they are easy targets find no sparring partners and turn their attentions elsewhere." She looked hard at me. "You won't be able to protect her from every hurt. Just be there for her to come to you to regain her strength."

Her warning was enough to absorb and I turned my attention to the parents on the other side of the window. I did not want to become involved in their conversations, and I waited for them to disperse. Without questioning my delay Mrs Huss busied herself with tidying her table and preparing for the morrow.

Feeling suddenly spent, I thanked her, pulled Minty's eiderdown up around her in preparation for the intense cold outside and slipped through the door, but not without noticing how tired and drawn Mrs Huss appeared. She had given her entire self, and was exhausted.

Waving goodbye, the extreme cold outside did little to diminish the glow attributable to Jimmy's generosity. The beer bottle boot scraper could take pride of place beneath the front doorstep of No. 15, Frances Street. One of nature's outcasts had brought me hurtling down rather more than a peg or two that morning, to learn the real meaning of charity.

I was ready for the exhaustion that had engulfed me on the previous occasion. Minty was tired too, and soon sank into a snug slumber. Indeed it was not long before the warmth and hope deserted me. Minty was not one of them. We had been just visitors in an unusual situation. To no degree did I feel that I had just taken her where she belonged. Was this, I wondered, an inability to see either Minty, or the children in the school, in perspective. What was in the way? What innate blindness prevented me from seeing what was there for all others to see?

I suspected that real acceptance was going to be a long painful business. And to achieve it I must return often to that wooden schoolhouse. Would I ever be able to interlock the final piece that was Minty, into the complex group of mentally retarded boys and girls whose afternoon I had just shared? On that cold, crisp Canadian morning, I feared not.

"Do you want to go again?" Bob asked over supper when I'd told him in detail about my visit.

"No," I replied, and his downcast look made me add the more quickly. "But I shall - because I have to, don't I?"

"I guess it might be the best thing. I wonder if it's possible to stop noticing the physical aspect after a while...you know, the way you never notice that some people you've known for years are ugly, when to strangers it is so apparent. When you see them every day, and get to know them as individuals..." He stopped suddenly, and then, "*Are* they individuals?"

I thought for a moment. "Um, yes. They mostly had similar characteristics, but even after a couple of hours there were traits that belonged to one or the other. But Bob, Minty didn't seem like any of them."

"That's because you didn't want her to be. It'll take time I suppose. And maybe it will never happen. Perhaps we'll always be so blind that she will never be backward to us."

We didn't talk any more about it; Bob's last comment somehow gave us permission to wait and see. 'Take one day at a time', Doc Cruickshank had counselled, and we would concur.

I slept fitfully that night, and pondered Wayne and his difficulties with speech and his ability to recognise the printed word. I wondered if speech would be Minty's greatest obstacle. Perhaps there was something wrong with Wayne's mouth structure...or was it laziness, and where did one draw the line between laziness and slowness. How was it possible to distinguish between them?

I was to search out information and ask innumerable questions over the coming months, resulting in the impression that such retardation had not been the most attractive subject to the research student. From whatever source I turned I seemed only to get a very general impression of what could be expected: nothing concrete and no definite guidelines. Findings were inconclusive and the reasons for the findings, woolly and unconvincing.

One afternoon I abandoned the intention of having steak for supper and bought liver instead, and then put a long distance call through to the specialist we had seen in London.

"No," he assured me, "he had found nothing untoward about the structure of Minty's mouth, but of course, mongols usually experienced difficulty with word formation; some never achieving recognisable speech at all."

I pressed for an explanation and immediately sensed his impatience. Perhaps there was a patient being kept waiting, or more likely if I turned up in person for an interview he could charge me appropriately.

"It is a matter of intelligence," he stated firmly, "or rather the lack of it. Some children are so severely retarded that almost all type of learning is beyond them."

"Accepted," I said, "but they aren't all so restricted. For the children I have seen this week, it's a matter of being able to do many of the things normal children achieve, only so much more slowly. They could mainly feed themselves; some could even sew and knit a little but it has taken a number of years to reach that stage."

"Where have you seen these children?"

I described the little schoolhouse where Minty and I had chalked up a few hours last week.

"Well, we really mustn't expect to become an expert in one week, don't you agree?"

I have never discovered why people resort to the royal 'We' when being derisive.

"That is precisely why I am calling you. Don't you see, I just want to help her? I'm aware of how much harm I can do by approaching the subject in the wrong way."

"Mrs Wade, I think you ought to relax and accept that your little girl is just six months old. Even a normal baby doesn't talk that young!"

I thanked him and agreed that I was being somewhat premature, and also that if I telephoned again, I would understand that he must bill me at the hourly consultation rate. I squeezed Minty's tiny hand and accepted we were on our own.

"That was a waste of a piece of fillet steak little one. I guess we are going to have to work it all out for ourselves."

After that I left the whole subject alone for some months. When I'd got over being sore at the consultant chiding me about teaching a six month old baby to talk, I saw the amusing side of it, and relaxed sufficiently to enjoy the fact of her being a baby.

In those early months we received many letters from adoring grandparents in England, eagerly awaiting their first meeting with a new grandchild, assuring me that it was all a horrible mistake, and quite impossible for any doctor to tell whether or not such a wee one had an adult future. They had never heard such nonsense, and insisted we didn't worry.

I didn't think I was worrying. It was more a feeling of hopelessness as if the bottom had fallen out of everything that mattered. And yet what they wrote must have been what I wanted to hear for I read those letters a dozen times or more. I suppose I even became a little convinced by them for I began to take snapshots, and Bob soon followed with movie film. The photographs, I proudly enclosed in letters to the folks back home.

And then the assurances came no more and they apologised for forcing me into a position of having to prove it to them. And that hadn't been the case at all. But how could they see what I still couldn't? I just kept on sending the snapshots and said I hoped one day they'd grow to love her as we did because she really was the most adorable thing this side of heaven. And they wrote back and said they already did, and that a huge parcel of cuddly toys was on its way.

CHAPTER SEVEN

It was 1961, a period of immense change worldwide. The economies of both England and Canada were quite buoyant. It was a good time to consider a change.

Spring arrived, and with it, our decision to return to England when term ended in June. Neither one of us had emigrated with any intention of applying for Canadian citizenship: I had left England on a one-year contract, met and married and stayed for three years, and for Bob it had been the first stepping stone to Japan, which was his original intended destination. Japan having become a somewhat misty blur on the horizon, we decided on building a future for the three of us in the 'Old Country', where Bob would get some supply teaching until he found a suitable job in industry.

Shortly before we were due to leave, a friend invited us to see her movie films taken whilst on holiday in England. She was older than we, and had married her Canadian husband during the war. Unlike many of her contemporaries she had been most fortunate; husband Des had built a beautiful home for the two of them, provided for their joint needs, and earned sufficient for Joan to make an annual return visit to the folks she had left behind as a young G.I. bride.

"She only really yearned to go back once," Des explained philosophically. "Rose coloured glasses and all that, but now she's always glad to come back home."

On the way home that night Bob asked abruptly, "Do you think we're fonder of Canada than we know?"

"That's an impossible question," I laughed, "but I know what you mean."

After watching Des's films we decided that England was as beautiful as I remembered it, but the people looked sort of tired and anxious...lots of them trudging with heavy shopping instead of having the boot loaded by a teenager at the grocery store. Not much evidence of second cars or carefree lifestyle...

"Maybe not even a first car for many," I said, recalling life in the road I lived in before uprooting. We fell silent for a while until Bob, reading my thoughts, put a reassuring arm round my shoulders.

"We'll make out, don't you worry."

I didn't feel as certain. "I suppose we could always come back?"

As single people we had each globe-trotted with just a suitcase and the optimism of youth. The anchorage that marriage and children tend to bestow hadn't yet impinged on us. And so having bidden our farewells - the hardest to Tom and Carol, and Arnold and Jill - we travelled by train to New York, intending to spend two days sightseeing before embarking on 'SS United States' to Southampton. Ten days, and several hundreds of dollars later, we were still in New York hoping against hope for an end to the strike that had begun as we were en route. Each day, as pickets paraded the quay, we looked longingly at the huge vessel, silent and impervious.

In common with many others we were irritated at not being able to sleep on board to halt the rapid escalation of hotel bills, but as funds sank dangerously low, we finally agreed to return by air. The speed with which a plane travels cannot do justice to the distance involved and we were desperately disappointed to have missed the ten-day cruise across the Atlantic that would have satisfyingly closed a chapter of our lives.

At their invitation, we stayed with my family for several weeks whilst Bob attended interviews, and I searched for a flat we could afford to rent on a temporary basis until we knew where the yet-to-be gained employment would take us. Bob had earned his degree at Edinburgh University and his teacher's certificate in Canada. We had not realized the difficulties that this 'foreign' qualification might present. The certificate was not readily accepted by the 'captains' of education. With no definite offer of a job, we were trying to conserve what little savings an enforced ten day stay in the then world's most expensive city had left us. Rents in the U.K. seemed to have risen ridiculously in my three year absence, and Bob, who had been away from England much longer, not only found them incredible, but became increasingly angry at the time we wasted going to view places described as 'homely and comfortable', which were little short of squalid. Something of the depression that had seeped into Joan's movie films was now enveloping us. None of the flats offered central heating or the everyday appliances and standard of living to which we had become accustomed.

Prospective landlords were defensive and suspicious. Without an employer's reference, and very certainly with a young child, the outlook was impossibly gloomy. Daily it became more apparent that there was no option other than to buy our own home. Obviously until Bob had landed a job, we were stuck, and forced to continue to put a strain on my parents who still had three daughters living at home, two of whom had offered to double-up, enabling us to have the largest bedroom.

Tension in Bob increased as he became mistakenly convinced that my family couldn't think much of a man who could land on them with a wife and baby but no job - 'and not even a proper baby'. The words were out one night before he could restrain them, and I found I could not help him, for was not I the one who had given birth to that 'less than perfect baby'?

Just as he had supported me through my depression in Canada, so now the roles were reversed. The more I was surrounded by family, the more isolated he seemed to be and gradually I realised he was caught in a vicious circle. The more depressed he became, the less effort he put into job applications.

I suspect because they sensed we needed some time and space to ourselves, my parents decided to take a long overdue break whilst my youngest sister went off to guide camp, Val, the middle one, would accompany them, and Kathy, the eldest of the three who worked locally as a secretary, would stay at home 'and baby-sit if we felt like an evening out'. The stage was so obviously set that it was difficult to thank them without letting them know that we knew they were doing it all for us. But it certainly did help even if to allow us to have a row with accusation and remonstration above a whisper.

When I wasn't flat hunting, I spent many secret hours with Minty, trying desperately to gain communication with her that might result in the merest suggestion of speech. If only she would say one word, I felt we would all three take an immense leap forward. Hours and hours of repetition - just the two of us there - so that when she finally produced her first word it would appear to have been as effortlessly as any other infant delights his audience with his 'mama' and 'dada'.

"Minty, look at Mummy - dad dad dad." I knelt on the floor, supporting her on the couch, my face very close to hers. Placing her hands on my cheeks, I hoped somehow she would feel the movement of my muscles, and intuitively if not intelligently, imitate the action, but her only response was to bite my nose and blow bubbles of delight. Perhaps if I said nothing else all day; no words of pleading or encouragement, just dad dad dad. So we hugged, smiled, and rubbed noses, all the time repeating the one sound. She watched me from her high chair as I prepared lunch, and all the time I continued the monotonous sound, which achieved absolutely nothing.

I was so engrossed in my own thoughts that I didn't hear Bob until he was in the room. He had been to the reference library to check the situations vacant columns in the daily papers.

"So what have you been up to?"

His question was almost rhetorical but I replied, "Talking to myself."

"To yourself? So hard up for company? You mean I don't count?"

"I have all the company I need," I said abrasively, "but she doesn't happen to say very much. So I'm teaching her."

He sighed impatiently. "Don't you think in view of all we've been told, you are starting a little early?"

"No."

I felt a sudden desire to throw the lunch across the room. "What you don't seem to realise," I blurted out angrily, "is that it's ten years head start she needs not just the few months I'm trying to give her if she's ever going to catch up with other children."

"That's nothing more than feminine logic."

"And what's wrong with feminine logic?"

"Everything, because it obviously hasn't told you that there is no question of her catching up with other kids. Helen.... she is backward!" There was a staccato stress on each word. "When in Heaven's name are you going to accept it?"

"Oh I've accepted it. Don't make any mistake about that. What I refuse to accept is that she is just going to *look* at us all her life. I want her to enjoy some sort of quality of living too, don't you understand?"

"O.K. only don't take your lack of success out on me." He was pouring himself a drink, and I hated it.

"Poor you," I retaliated accusingly. "And what are you doing to help?" I had gone too far. The remark had been insanely unreasonable. Silently furious, he got up from the table, took his mac from the hallstand, and went out. I made no attempt to go after him, or call him back.

What was happening to us? We'd made a mess of having a baby, made a mistake in leaving Canada. We had no job, no money, and the way we were behaving, we'd soon have no marriage! No, that was *not* the road we were going down. I quickly made some fresh coffee. I knew where I was heading, and I had to keep going. And one particular word was the first step.

"Daddy Daddy. Come on Minty, we've got to do it. Please Minty, for Daddy. We've just got to show him it's worth trying."

But Minty was fast asleep, smiling serenely, and blissfully unaware of the tension growing between her adoring parents.

I had a pretty good idea where Bob would have gone, and telephoned to remind him that we had an appointment, or rather Minty did, with the G.P. I had known for a number of years before going to Canada. He had been then, the junior partner, but was now apparently successfully established in his own practice. However, either I was mistaken about his whereabouts, or Bob quite understandably wanted nothing to do with me and was refusing to answer the phone. And soon I would have to tell him that we had yet another problem.

We had suspected for some time that Minty's eyesight wasn't one hundred per cent and knew that sooner or later, we had to bring it to someone's attention. Only how could anyone test it when there was no reaction from the patient? Bryan would do for a start, and then we could take whatever advice he offered. I woke Minty to get her ready, all the time repeating 'dad dad dad'. Just for one brief moment I thought I saw a glimmer of understanding in those blue grey eyes that were so much like her father's but there was no response. Would it ever come, I wondered.

"She's had the book thrown at her alright." As Bryan examined her, I recalled the slower, less professionally arrogant approach of Doc Cruickshank, on that winter's night when he broke the awful news to us. I was aware of his continuing comments. "How much do you reckon she can see?"

"It's difficult to say with any certainty. And that isn't for lack of observation as you can imagine. One day I can put something large right under her nose and she seems not to notice it, and at other times she'll obviously have seen something quite small...a button or a bead. I don't think size has much to do with it quite honestly, and, of course, there are times when she's just not interested. It helps if something is a different colour from its background...and movement too, of course."

He made notes now, seeming to have abandoned the examination.

"I'll fix you an appointment to see a specialist. You'll have to go to the County Clinic. Don't hope for too much - she's a senior specialist, but not a miracle worker. I'm sorry - I've disappointed you, haven't I? But your little one is outside my field."

"Don't you cover mental handicap at medical school?" I asked, trying to make it a polite enquiry.

"It gets a mention, that's about all I'm afraid," he frankly admitted. And then to change the subject, "I hear your husband is a bridge fiend. What about coming round for a rubber or two tonight? I don't think you've met my wife either."

"Thanks all the same, but I think my bridge might suffer too much from thinking about other things." I could hardly say that I might not even see Bob this evening. "Perhaps when we have got something lined up for Minty's eyes we'll be able to concentrate on taking you off a few tricks."

"It's a date. Keep cheerful now and don't be too long before you start another baby. Lightning rarely strikes twice in the same place you know."

"You're rather late with the advice. As a G.P. you should be more observant!"

He grasped my hand warmly. That's really good news...I might have known you wouldn't be put off. Good for you."

"It was an accident," I said. "Otherwise there would have been no more babies. So forget the 'well done' bit. I'll be seeing you, and thanks."

CHAPTER EIGHT

A fortnight later found the three of us sitting on one of the low leather benches in the Women's Institute Hall, where, amongst all the obviously normal children, we saw more handicapped children than we had yet seen in the same place at any one time. Obviously poor eyesight was a common problem for them.

"Next please!"

Bob and I jumped like a couple of Jack-in-the-Boxes. The cramped, antiquated consulting room smelt musty and Dickensian. A bespectacled, elderly lady doctor impatiently signalled to us to sit down. We were both edgy, believing her to be the ultimate in passing a decision. Giving Minty a cursory glance, she merely stated, "Um .....what's the trouble?" The question, which we felt was ours to ask and hers to answer left us tongue-tied. At last, having gained no response from either of us, she condescended to lift her head and meet our eyes.

"We'd like to know what can be done to prevent our daughter's eyesight from deteriorating: we know from our own observations that it isn't good," Bob said directly, a deliberate intake of breath indicating his irritation. The doctor's manner, though she said virtually nothing, seemed to refute the possibility that eyesight could actually be improved.

"Not a great deal I'm afraid." She sensed Bob's annoyance, and softened slightly. "Your doctor will have explained that most of these children have additional defects....sight .....heart trouble."

"Well no, not really," I began, but my words were ignored as she continued.

"You are going to have to accept that cataracts are almost inevitable. She's very young: there is nothing I can do at this stage."

At last she seemed aware of the impact her words were having and her cool, apparent indifference gave way to a more sympathetic approach. But still her authority and experience defied the question. We nodded whatever thanks were due, and numbly re-entered the buzz of the waiting room. There was no question of our not believing her, and many times since I've wondered why I allowed her word to go unchallenged. Deflated and miserable, we walked across the car park into the High Street.

Suddenly, Bob blurted out to no one in particular, "Well if money's what she needs, we'll have to think of a way to get some."

"You mean you are going to pay some Harley Street quack a hundred guineas to tell you what we have just been told," I snapped, taking my disappointment out on Bob as if he were to blame."

"Quacks don't operate from Harley Street," he retorted. "Anyway if you don't consider she's worth a try...."

This sort of thing was becoming more and more frequent. We would convince ourselves that we had accepted the situation, and then the moment the acceptance was challenged, we were like drowning rats ready to throw principles to the wind.

"You think it's my fault, don't you?" Bob almost shouted, and a passer-by turned abruptly at the outburst.

"For Heaven's sake, I'm not deaf!"

"Well don't you?"

He threw the question again, finding it impossible to lower his almost hysterical tone. "Don't you?"

"Don't be ridiculous. How can we tell whose fault it is? In any case I wouldn't even want to know."

At least that was true. Better to believe we as a couple had done something wrong together. In a strange way, that in itself united us, whilst everything else was tearing us apart.

"Be honest Bob, there must have been times when you thought it was mine."

"Oh yes," he admitted, and his whisper was hoarse. "But now, I don't know why: I just know it's me. There must be tests. We'll go to a clinic or something. You can divorce me. I'll send you some money." His voice was staccato and frightening.

"Bob, stop. O God, let's get out of this street. Bob don't push me away." And then I gave up trying to keep abreast. He was ahead with Minty in his arms.

Who had rejected whom? His actions belied his words as he carried Minty away from me. He was losing me in the crowd, believing after all that I was the cause. The knowledge drained me of any will to follow him, and indifferent to the rain slushing around my ankles, I entered a coffee bar and ordered an espresso. I picked up a discarded newspaper from the chair beside me, but the headlines were unintelligible. Superimposed were the words 'handicapped babies, handicapped babies'. They grew bigger and then took on a sound quality.

I stifled the scream in my throat, and stared at the waiter who had just brought my coffee, as if by averting my gaze, I could avoid reading the words. But I could hear them still, despite the sounds emanating from the jukebox someone had fed with the appropriate coin. It was some moments before I realised the waiter was staring back at me.

"Come on miss, better drink that coffee. Are you O.K.?"
I felt weak and dizzy, and asked him if I could have a brandy.

"Course yer can't miss - don't yer know licensing hours? Not that I could give you one if it *were* opening time - there's a pub next door though. Come to think of it, yer looks as if yer could do with something stronger than coffee."

"I'll just drink the coffee. I'll be alright now thank you."
He put the overflowing cup in front of me and grinned. "There y'are miss - one cup *and* saucer of coffee! Wish I could lace it for you but yer knows how it is."

I forced a smile and in doing so, felt better, but not knowing where to go I remained in my corner seat, watching the steady flow of customers gamble their threepenny bits in the one-arm-bandits. I tried to decide whether my reluctance to go home was a respect for Bob's decision - (for a decision he seemed to have made, whether consciously or otherwise) - or whether I was unequal to all that my baby's condition demanded of me.

All my life I'd been pretty successful at going along with the crowd...at being the normal average kind of girl, but when asked for that little bit extra, I wasn't worth a hill o'beans. No wonder Bob had despised me, and now he had lost me in that normal, ordinary crowd in which I belonged. I could not rid myself of the look in his eyes as he had walked away. Not hatred, but disdain: such bitter disdain.

Quite suddenly I remembered I had made up, and put the last of Minty's milk feeds in the fridge before we had left the house this afternoon. It would be after the shops closed that Bob in his present mood, would notice that we were out of milk. I glanced at my watch, and hastened to the nearest shop.

As if the pints of milk gave me the right to enter the house, I let myself in with the front door key. I don't know whether Bob heard me. He was in the lounge, head cupped in his hands; a study of desolation, and Minty, fast asleep and smiling, lay on the couch beside him. I did what the English have a reputation for doing in times of stress: I made a huge pot of tea.

"I'm sorry," Bob said without lifting his head. "That was unforgivable. I've given her a mashed banana and the milk feed. She almost drank it all before she fell asleep. She wasn't too fussy about the mashed up stuff though." His voice was tense and strange, and he rose to his feet. "Helen what are we going to do for her? She can't go on being rejected by every bureaucratic so and so. Hell, I wonder if some of them really know what they are talking about. Look at that old girl this afternoon. How long is it since she was at medical school? Yet she pontificated as if she could change the destiny of mankind."

We should have attached a great deal more importance to the question he had just raised, and yet for some reason we let it slip as if it had been rhetorical. I suppose we both thought it was the kind of remark born of disappointment and after all, an expert was an expert. I didn't mention the business of paying privately: I knew Bob was thrashing it out in his own mind and it was never politic to discuss his ideas midstream.

"Are you staying in?" he asked abruptly. It was a strange question, and brought back the detachment of the afternoon.

"Well of course ...is there any reason why I shouldn't?"

"No, no...I just thought. Oh I'm going for a beer....or maybe a walk...I don't know."

Was this the natural inclination of all human beings - to be alone when suffering, or was my husband, for the second time today, rejecting me? He left the house, and I heard the car start noisily. Crumpled in the corner of the couch where he had been sitting, was a letter from a chemical company offering him a job. He hadn't mentioned it: perhaps not even a job mattered any more.

I decided to sleep in my parents' room that night. What a blessing was their absence. It was partly because I couldn't stand the friction, and more I suspected, because my wounded pride told me that Bob would prefer it that way.

Kathy came in from work; we sat in companionable silence for a while - long enough for her to realise that baby-sitting services were not much in demand. "I don't like seeing my big sister miserable," she said. "It doesn't seem to be making much sense - all the letters you sent from Canada were full of adoration for that bloke of yours. I was really looking forward to meeting him - but he hasn't bowled *this* maiden over!"

"We've a lot of problems to sort out." I explained. "And right now Kathy we can't seem to make much sense of anything."

"Maybe you're both trying too hard. Perhaps you should take life more philosophically, like my little god-daughter here."

"You want to be godmother?"

"Who else? Minty's mine; the next one's Val's, and the last one is Lin's. You have to have three, to keep it all neat and tidy!"

"You just made my day," I hugged her. Now I could tell Bob my news!

Exhausted though I was, sleep evaded me. At 2a.m. Bob still wasn't home. Several times I got up to make coffee or read a little. Once I thought I heard a noise, but as Minty in all her eighteen months, had never woken in the night, I dismissed it. But when I heard it again I ran upstairs. She was wide awake, sucking the satin edge of her blanket.

"Minty, you woke up! Before morning! You actually gave me a disturbed night!"

The latter was rather more fancied than true, but the fact that she could do anything so normal as to wake in the night, caused such a surge if elation to sweep through me that I fairly danced her round the room. This she loved, and grinned toothlessly and 'bit' my nose.

I held her out at arm's length. "You woke up Minty!" I'll never know if she felt a need to rise to the occasion, but without any warning to prevent her mother almost collapsing with shock, she said, very clearly and unmistakably: "Daddy". And at that moment, time stopped. No other word existed. Our daughter had spoken! In one night, two very normal, but for us, very wonderful, things had happened. No - three, because now I heard a car coming to a halt. Minty's daddy had come home. Before his key was in the latch, I was hurtling downstairs.

"Bob, come quickly. It's happened. Oh hurry." I fell into his arms as the hall door opened.

"What's happened? Where's Minty?"

"She's in bed - waiting for you. And nothing's wrong."

"Then what...?"

"Come and see quickly. Oh please God let her do it again, please - for her Daddy."

I was suddenly desperate. What if she didn't? She must. At that moment it seemed that our marriage depended on it. There wasn't a lot for her to choose from. Only one glorious word that she may or may not say again. Bob was perplexed. "Why did you wake her up? What's going on?"

"I didn't wake her."

"But she never...oh lor, I probably fed her too quickly - she's had indigestion. Sorry Minty. Your Dad wasn't a very nice guy today."

"I don't think its indigestion. In fact she seems rather pleased about something."

"So do you, considering the kind of day we've had."

"Let's forget the day. Tonight something wonderful happened."

If I had believed in a storybook heaven, I'd have thought every angel it possessed was rooting for me that night. Hardly had we reached her cot before she smiled, blew a raspberry, and said for the second time in her life, "Daddy."

Bob's mouth fell open. He spun round, gripped my shoulders, and said, "Did you hear that? Helen did you hear what she said? Our Minty can speak!!"

"She'll be debating in the Upper Chamber before your first grey hair," I teased, somewhat unfairly since the surprise with which I had greeted her debut into the oral world only half an hour ago, had been no less than my husband's. The three of us danced in a precarious huddle around the bedroom unable to stifle our elation.

"Can anyone join the party?" We hadn't heard Kathy come in, making our joy complete, for now we had not only had a miracle, but someone to tell about it, too.

So the barriers were down, and Minty was over the first hurdle. One word had proved to my no longer doubting mind that she could hear clearly, and what I feared would be so much more of a problem, she could imitate the sound she heard. At which point in the two months of repetition had she heard, but not been able to reproduce the sound, I wondered. It didn't matter. Tonight our Minty had pronounced her first word as clearly as a normal child; all that was abnormal was the length of time taken to achieve success.

No matter, it *could* be done. If one word, why not many more? We were on our way at last. For the first time, the tension eased, and a relentless fatigue enveloped me. I began to reflect on the implications of one word every two months and turned to where she lay gurgling at my side. "Little Suzie," I said unconsciously using her old name, "We've got one hell of a long struggle ahead of us!"

"Daddy," came the reply!

"That's right," I said. "Daddy, and don't you forget it!"

She never did!

CHAPTER NINE

The natural follow-up was obvious. Or was it? I soon learned not to apply any logic to the learning process. After four weeks, 'Mummy' remained an impossibility, and to my horror, 'Daddy', hitherto pronounced in an accent out of the top drawer, was taking on unrecognisable forms: the most frequent, 'Dabby'.

Turning the problem over in my mind one night, it suddenly dawned on me. She didn't want to say 'Mummy'. She wanted another 'a' sound. Heavens, she was telling me clearly enough. And she had also given way to the fact that she could make a 'b' sound. Fine. From now on her toy kitten would be 'tabby'. No, that too was similar. But 'bat' was sufficiently different. Tomorrow we had to find a bat; essentially a bright coloured one to attract her. I could sleep now. Operation Bat was in hand.

Bob had already gone into town to invest in a briefcase for the new job. I dressed Minty who was serenely unaware of my buoyant spirit and determination for her next success and began our search at the village shop. Minutes later we left with a bright red plastic battledore and accompanying shuttlecock. Not even waiting to get it home, I deposited the superfluous shuttlecock and packaging in a bus-stop waste bin, and pushed the buggy on a somewhat irregular course with one hand, whilst holding the bat in front of Minty with the other. With every step, sometimes loudly, sometimes softly, I said its name; sang it, whispered it, constantly changing the tone of my voice so as not to lull her to sleep.

But sleep she did, and by the time we were home, she was about as interested in a bat as an arthritic grandmother. When she awoke, I curled her tiny fingers around its handle, but though she smiled at me, her brain didn't seem to tell her hand that it was holding something new and exciting. And then I saw the fingers tighten; her hand was certainly sensitive to its contents. Going at a cracking pace, and chanting 'bat' sixty times a minute wasn't necessarily getting us anywhere. I would try saying it once, and then sitting there quietly with her, not saying another word, whilst her brain operated in whatever low gear it could handle.

I must do what I had been told to do from the beginning: accept that everything was going to be a slow process....a long time, but *not* an eternity. And, of course, days could no longer be allocated solely to Minty: Bob was soon to move south to begin his job with a chemical company, and I would join him at weekends for house hunting sessions. And though never meant to be on the agenda, our second baby was on the way. Looking back, it was a much healthier situation than having only a handicapped child to concentrate on.

Two weeks later, to all appearances, we hadn't moved an inch towards mastery of the second word. But that was because I had blinkers on, and was playing God in deciding just what the second word should be. If the truth could have been known, I expect Minty was as fed up with the word 'bat' as I was.

I had just put the phone down having made plans to join Bob the following weekend to view the properties he had short listed from the agents' brochures, and proceeded to settle Minty in her high chair ready for her supper. "Come on sweetheart -open up...a spoonful for Daddy...one for Mummy." A little hand beat on the table-tray, and firmly clenched gums resisted the next spoonful.

"So what's more interesting than food?" I asked rhetorically.

"House," she replied!

We were on our way!

We found our house that weekend - the eleventh we looked at, and the one we still have today albeit rather larger, and much changed superficially. There was no doubt about it; we knew the moment we entered the kitchen door 'because the front door sticks a bit dear - we hardly ever uses it yer see'. It was just as if it had been waiting for us. Despite its obvious drawbacks, it would not be denied, and so all that was necessary was to agree a price and wait for the formalities to be completed. I don't know what we saw in it that day, with ivy-leaf wallpaper up the stairs, and 1930 cream and brown gloss paint in the kitchen; in fact, I don't think we *saw* anything that we didn't immediately plan to change as soon as it could be afforded, but more what we *felt*. We were together. Bob had found a job. And Minty could speak!

There were the usual delays and hitches, and so it was decided that I should have our second baby in the Midlands and then move into the house before spring. The deposit wiped our bank account clean, and anything we could salvage from Bob's first month's salary would have to purchase baby-needs - second-hand without a doubt.

Had I known then what medical science has since proved - that having one handicapped child greatly increases the chance of having another, I would have driven myself to distraction with worry. But the current thinking was exactly what the local doctor had pronounced – 'lightning doesn't strike twice in the same place'. And so I eagerly anticipated the birth of our first son, being so confident he *would* be a boy, that everything I collected was in blue.

My only experience of childbirth had been in the comfort and dignity of a Canadian hospital, run very much on hotel lines with management doing everything possible to ensure satisfied customers. A nurse to welcome the mother-to-be at the main door of the hospital; tissues and other toiletries waiting on bedside table. Gifts of flowers and baby-things provided by local companies greeted the event, and in the small Canadian town in which we lived, a birth was immediately announced on the local radio station, with the obvious resulting messages from friends and neighbours. This was not, as may be assumed, a private hospital, but a state hospital for all who belonged to the inexpensive Government sponsored Blue Cross

Insurance Scheme; certainly no more expensive than our own National Health Service contributions.

So it was something of an eye opener to have a baby on a British shoestring. Dignity went straight out of the window, and 'Call me when you feel it coming' was the order of the day. 'Pull on that string and I'll hear the buzzer... we're short staffed - and don't push till I tell you!'

I pulled on the string several times in the night, but out of cowardly fear of being in that cell of a delivery room alone, not because anything was happening. The midwife's impatience grew increasingly apparent as the hours progressed.

"I don't think you're trying," she accused.

But inevitably the debut of our second baby occurred, and revived by her break, she said graciously, "No wonder you had problems - look at the size of his shoulders."

I sank back into the pillow, exhausted, but well content; she had said *his* shoulders. Minty had a baby brother. And I did not doubt for one moment that all was well.

Bob drove up from the South at the weekend to see us. His joy and pride were irrepressible: people he had never seen before were offered cigars, and I knew that he, as I, was longing to shout out to the world, 'It's fine - we got it right this time - we haven't caused this baby any harm. We can do it too!' For no matter what the psychologists and counsellors assure, whatever medical science has proved, the guilt of having produced a handicapped child is phenomenal. It is not something that time heals, or that is dispersed by logic and reason. It is there - often to be explained or excused; always to be lived with. A fact that may explain the intense bond that exists between parent and handicapped child.

Not that the love is borne of guilt, but rather of a burning desire to compensate for getting it wrong in the beginning, and sheer inability to understand why the child, far from blaming, responds as if he or she is so lucky to be the recipient of the very special kind of loving.

Though still missing, almost to the point of it being a physical ache, the vast expanse of staggeringly beautiful Canadian wilderness we had left behind, we were now a family installed once more in an English life-style. We each accustomed to it in our own way. Bob found 'the right and wrong way of doing things' immensely restrictive. It angered him that in order to get on, one had to fit into a mould...... 'Director material' was a phrase that incensed him.

There was less tolerance of 'characters'; letting slip that one was in the Rotary or Round Table, or a sidesman at church was politic. Just being good at the job was certainly no guarantee of success. Sometimes I could feel him chafing at the reins, yearning for weekends in the bush, huntin', shootin', and fishin'. And I yearned for the stillness of crossing the lake at sunset, and going to sleep in a log cabin, warm and smelling of spruce, then waking to the sunlight of a Canadian fall.

Neither admitted it to the other, for there was no point since it was impossible, but we both longed to return to the tiny community of misfits (according to English standards) of which we had once been a part. Individuals, who for all their differences of origin and attitude and conviction, were bonded together in the strength that living in the wilderness demands. Often I repeated the names of those 'towns': communities of only several hundreds....Sioux Lookout, Attikocan...Kenora. Places I had heard described by some as God's own country, and by others as a living hell. Places where one was free to shout out at the top of one's voice for sheer joy, and nobody would have heard - and certainly would not have thought it peculiar, even if they had. It was very much a land in which 'a man could do what a man felt he had to do' without incurring judgement from his fellows.

The community had not thought it had any right to interfere with history teacher Dan's need to consume vast quantities of whisky each night, much less allow it to cloud their assessment of his ability to do his job.Nobody taught their children like he did. No one gained a higher success rate for university entrance. What he did in the hours that were his private life, were his affair. Neither was it a cause for raised eyebrows that Ed, the science teacher, had taken off for a whole year, and then come back to pick up the pieces and start again. The total absence of pettiness was liberating, and getting back into harness in the U.K. was not easy.

Not that we had found all of Ontario free from convention and stereotype. The towns in the civilised south were every bit as punctuated by protocol as any British community. In many places the influence of the Scots was keenly felt - especially on Sunday! Bob who had spent four years at Edinburgh University, frequently commented on the similarities.

Living in a new county meant finding a new doctor, and having discovered a most competent one (to whom we warmed, I suspect, because he was so unstuffy) we decided it was opportune to raise again the subject of Minty's eyesight. Having the benefit of previous expert advice, I was almost apologetic about asking if he thought anything could be done to prevent further deterioration, and almost fell off my chair, when, without looking up from the notes he was making on our son's healthy progress, he said, "Almost certainly."
I was still staring at him when he finished writing.

"What's wrong?" he grinned. "Don't you approve of my cords either in the surgery? It is Saturday; I'll be damned if I'll wear a suit. I'm taking my tribe on a picnic as soon as I've seen the last patient."

"You should be in Canada," I smiled. "You're ahead of your time here in England. And I 'er I didn't quite catch what you said."

He laughed candidly. "You did, but for a reason that perplexes me, you can't believe me."

"I'll explain another time," I said. "Right now it's more important to hear what her chances are."

"No, I won't presume to do that. Eyes are not my specialist area. But I can put you in touch with someone who's at the top of his profession."

"Old?"

"Only a few years to retirement. Why do you ask?"

I explained about our visit to the specialist we had seen soon after arriving in England.

"That was unfortunate. Happens sometimes. Put it behind you. It's only a month since this man was lecturing on the latest developments - you must never generalise."

He had packed considerable information into a few words, and I took the point. "When can we see him?"

"It may be several months. You'll have to get used to long waiting lists in England. I'll get a letter off before I leave surgery today."

I thought of his children impatiently waiting to go on a picnic, and was doubly grateful. I didn't know it at the time, but he had already secured a post as a consultant in Australia, and before Minty was actually seen by the specialist to whom he wrote that day, he had taken his large family to the other side of the world. But not before he had changed the prospects for our daughter's future. He could afford to disregard the disapproval from his senior partners for his casual weekend dress.

He didn't actually look at Minty's eyes, which seemed a little odd, but after all we had been to people who claimed, after examining her, that they knew enough about eyes to realise that nothing could be done. And at this moment, his knowledge of a man who *could* do something was highly preferable. He noted the particulars - not yet two, mentally-handicapped, cataracts...left eye rather worse.

"When did you notice the left eye was weaker?" he asked.

"Only several weeks ago. She seems to enjoy watching our baby son. If I put him on her left side, she appears to have to turn her whole body to be able to watch his movements properly."

"Fine. I've got all the details we need at this stage. Incidentally, after two babies, you look as if you could do with a tonic."

"You just gave me one the only one I need. But thanks."

"Well don't grow iron toenails as a result of it," he grinned. And as I got up to go he added, "By the way, your little girl won't be admitted if she has a cold, so once you get a date, steer her clear of folks with coughs and sneezes."

Sudden deflation gripped me. "But she's always got a cold -she had never been rid of one. It seems to be an associated condition."

"Um, that presents a problem. Actually, I suspect she doesn't so much have a cold as a catarrhal sniffle, for which we can most certainly do something."

He had the surgery pharmacist make up some drops. "There we are. Treat her with the magic potion three times a day."

"Guaranteed?"

"No. But I'll be here to try something else if that doesn't do the trick."

He won't know how he changed the prospects for Minty, for it was not long before we lost him to the Aussies.

CHAPTER TEN

Within the month we were summoned to the Out Patients Department of the general hospital ten miles away where we quickly discovered that Mr Paton not only had a remarkable skill in his chosen field, but natural talent for handling his patients.

"Hello Whiskers," he greeted her, and I smiled at the addition of yet another name. She made no protest as he peered studiously into each eye. He reflected for some moments - each one seemed an age - before saying, "I think there's quite a lot we can do for little Whiskers here, Mother. Yes....it will take time of course but given no further deterioration in the immediate future, I'm sure we can do much to improve matters. You realise there may be a number of visits to hospital?" He did not wait for an answer, but passed a note to a young man who was obviously one of his students, drawing his attention to a sketch he had made of the right eye. "We'll begin on that one," he said, pointing to an amoeba-like blob.

"What is it?" I asked.

"One of several cataracts," he replied, giving me the direct answer I had asked for. "Not the kind old people have," he added, sensing my anxiety. "We are going to dissolve them. It will probably be a long haul, but her vision will be greatly improved. You are not much more than a blur to her at the moment."

"How soon can you begin?"

"Unfortunately, there are more defective eyesights that I have staff for. You'll be hearing from me just as soon as I can arrange it."

We were therefore amazed to get a call from the hospital only six weeks later. Another child had contracted mumps so there had been a cancellation and if we could call at the hospital immediately to collect some eye ointment, which must be applied twenty-four hours before entry to the ward, she could be admitted the following day. I glanced at the clock. One of the three daily buses to pass through the village was due in less than half an hour. A frantic nappy-change, a bottle of feed made up for Neil, and a banana for Minty were hastily thrust into a bag.

With just two minutes to spare, we were at the bus stop hoping the conductor wouldn't curse at the sight of Mum, two babies and a twin pushchair to be taken on board. He did, and was not exactly co-operative. He obviously tossed in his mind the alternatives of leaving me to struggle on alone, and being late at the terminus, or giving me a hand. With an ostentatious lack of grace, he lifted the pushchair onto the suitcase rack beside the platform, whilst I fumbled for change to pay our fares. However, his manner did nothing to dampen my spirits, for today was the beginning of the end of Minty's defective eyesight. We had at least found *one* problem that something could be done about, and a sullen countenance counted for nothing in the face of such hope.

"Have a nice day," I said sarcastically when we reached the terminus and he leapt off the bus for his break leaving me to lift the pushchair and two infants.

An elderly lady crumpled with arthritis patted me on the shoulder.

"Here dear, put the two wee ones on my lap while you get the push-chair off." I did, and put the brake on whilst I collected Minty and Neil, and then climbed the step a third time to retrieve the old lady, whilst the driver indicated his impatience to drive the bus into the garage at the back of the bus station.

It was only when we were all on the pavement, and I had reined the children in the push-chair that the lady slowly straightened herself and realised she had left her stick on board.

92

"I can't manage without it," she said forlornly.

"Hold on to the children," I instructed and dashed to the garage where at least thirty identical buses were parked whilst having their numbers changed. I was desperate. If I didn't get to the hospital soon, and it was ten minutes walk away, I'd never catch the only bus home. I reported the matter to an Inspector who said he would 'endeavour to locate the article, Madam', deposited the old lady in the bus station cafe with a cup of tea, and promised to check all was well when I returned to catch the bus home.

Hot and dishevelled, we arrived at the Hospital Dispensary, collected the ointment and on instruction proceeded to Out Patients to be told how to apply it. The nurse was obviously at the end of a very tiring day.

"I'll be with you as soon as I can," she smiled. "Do you want a magazine?" And then "Oh of course not - you haven't exactly got a free hand have you?"

Eventually she returned to us, and instructed me in the art of layering the ointment evenly across the lower lid. I carried it, and the two children out of the waiting room as if they were gold, frankincense and myrrh.

I missed the bus of course. It was leaving the bus station as I approached in as much of a hurry as my charges would allow. A taxi being out of the question, the only alternative was to sit in the cafe until such time as Bob would arrive home and I could ask him to drive out to collect us. I was all in, and flopped into the nearest chair, a crumb-laden orange plastic one, purpose built to make sure customers didn't stay longer than it took to drink a cup of tea. Having thus installed myself, I noticed it was self-service. It was going to require something of a conjuring trick to manoeuvre Minty in the pushchair, Neil under my arm, and a cup of tea, from the counter to my table by the door.

"I'm glad I stayed," said a voice nearby. "You sit there, and I'll get the tea." It was my old lady.

"What are you doing here?" I gasped. "I left you ages ago!"

"They only managed to retrieve my stick half an hour since," she explained, "and I saw your last bus leaving and realised you'd have something of a problem. I live in the town, and there are buses every few minutes to where I live, so I thought I'd just wait awhile. How did you get on?"

I couldn't disguise my pleasure at seeing her, even though I protested that she shouldn't have waited. Why, I didn't even know her name.

"I'll get us both a cuppa, and then you can tell me how you propose getting back to your village."

The milky tea slopped in the saucer, but it was reasonably hot and refreshing, as long as it was drunk quickly.

"Oh it's such a relief to see you," I confessed. "If I may I'll ask you to guard the children whilst I find a phone box to call my neighbour – we don't have a phone. She will pop round and tell Bob what has happened to us, and I expect he'll come straight here."

She was only too willing, and while we waited, I told her how I'd be bringing Minty back again to the hospital within twenty-four hours, all about her eyes, and the first operation to dissolve her cataracts.

"She has more than one?"

"Three. And the lens will have to be destroyed to get at them, so her vision will never be good, but anything is better than blindness."

"Of course," she said compassionately. "Such a little mite."

Now with the benefit of many years of medical progress, Minty would have had her lens frozen and lifted off, and then replaced unharmed when the cataracts had been treated. But such a development had not occurred, and we were to be grateful for the possibility of even limited sight.

"I shall be here to meet your bus," the old lady said decisively, "and now that I have my stick I shall be able to help you. No doubt you'll have a case to carry as well for her, if she's to stay in hospital for a while. At least I can offer one free hand, if only a slow pair of feet!"

With someone to talk with, the time passed quickly until Bob arrived to bundle us all in the car. We dropped the old lady off within minutes, but not before she and Bob had shared a joke or two. I did so envy the speed with which he managed to reach a 'familiar' stage with people.

"My husband used to say," she chuckled, "that the people who know most about prayer, are the owners of old, second-hand cars!" It was a comment that helped us to make light of many a breakdown!

As it happened, the hospital agreed that Minty could be admitted the following evening rather than the afternoon, but we arranged to pick up our old lady anyway, and she accompanied us, being openly delighted at the prospect of holding Neil in her arms whilst we took Minty into the miniature three-bedded ward. In my enthusiasm for something actually to be done, I hadn't contemplated how it would feel to leave her.

I undressed and changed her, and she stood up in the cot, peering over the bar just as she did at home, gurgling as she made her rocking movements. It was only when the nurse came to say it was time to go, that I realised my hands were magnetised to the cot-sides.

"Could we not wait until she falls asleep?" I asked.

"She will soon settle after you have left. You may visit tomorrow." The nurse's manner left no room for argument or request: the days of mothers being encouraged to spend as much time as possible with their hospitalised children were not then.

"Night, Minty darling," I whispered and was grateful for Bob's arm around my shoulder. She watched as we left the tiny ward, utterly trusting, and neither perplexed nor hurt that we were going. It would take some time for her to connect our departure with being alone. How much would it matter that someone else would bring her breakfast, and change her nappies. Would the nurses understand that she couldn't feed herself…...would they be patient? Questions that would be insulting to nurses in this enlightened era. But not so then; retardation was synonymous with the necessity for being institutionalised - very much second-class citizens.

We went out into the corridor, where Mrs Partridge, for that was her name, was quick to thrust Neil into my arms.

"She'll be just fine." There was such assurance in her smile. "And failing eyesight is one of her problems *you* can't solve, so leave her in the hands of those who can, whilst you go home to enjoy the luxury of having only one baby again."

I recognised them as wise words, and I made every attempt to do just that. A simple thing like getting on the bus with only one infant plus push-chair was a doddle after struggling with two, and the daily visit for just half an hour an outing rather than a challenge.

The first day was the worst: poor little Minty had pads over her eyes, and because she kept trying to pull them off, her arms were strapped to small weights in the cot. It was the first time I had ever seen her struggle against her circumstances, and whilst the scene itself was distressing, I silently thrilled at the realisation there was fight and determination in her, to whatever slight degree. But the fight was easily subdued until the time came for the pads and bandages to be removed. Bob and I looked only into the consultant's eyes as he gently lifted the gauze. We were old hands now and knew that by scrutinising *his* expression, we would know the truth as soon as he did. The left eye was good; the right one less so.

"Will you have to do it again?" Bob asked, and he nodded.

"Just one of the cataracts hasn't responded to the needling. The others are most encouraging. Take her home - she's done well - and I'll re-admit her in three months. I'm well pleased."

If he was pleased then so were we, for this man had our whole trust. However, the problem was not solved in three months, for new cataracts appeared, and we learned to accept frequent hospitalisation and fortnightly visits to the Out Patients Department as a routine part of life until Minty was five. Mrs. Partridge accompanied me so often, having met us from the bus, that she was finally prevailed upon to join the Women's Voluntary Service to serve teas from the crowded waiting room, but not until each of my children could walk, and step down unaided from a bus!

By this time we had our second son, Jonathan, a real character, and a bundle of energy. Needless to say the three of them kept me on my toes, especially as Minty remained a baby until she was two; in many respects much longer - taking her first steps just one month after her second birthday. The memory of one who had just learned to stagger around the room, a second who took two steps and then decided crawling was quicker, and a third who scooted everywhere on his bottom at a rate of knots, will live with me for all time.

Strangely it had not been a difficult decision to have a third child, despite our original stance. Witnessing now the unadulterated exuberance, natural competition, and sheer fun resulting from the companionship each of the boys provided for the other - a companionship we had both considered essential - any misgiving or trepidation we experienced whilst waiting for Jonathan, became insignificant. And albeit subconsciously, they were being trained to be mindful and considerate of a sister with less skill and little or no ingenuity, who was an unchallenged part of their world by virtue of having been there when they arrived. For them at least, handicap was not synonymous with 'abnormal'. Only later would the world alert them to another viewpoint.

Those were precious years. The years before they went to school in rapid succession. Teaching was what I suppose I was reasonably good at and it was what I did before they were born and what I returned to when Jonathan the youngest went to school.

But writing was my first love, and though I never had time to write them down, I invented story after story to tell them as the four of us all crowded in an old, comfy, enormous armchair that Bob had bought second-hand when I was still in the Midlands. The chair was beside the Rayburn kitchen range - the warmest place in the house, since we had no central heating. It was the most beloved of chairs being the one they were allowed to climb on, and which was in turn a den, a horse, a boat and a hundred other products of the imagination.

It was the chair that Bob sat in when he came home from work, exhausted not by the job, but by the commuting, and it was the one I sank into when all three infants were finally in bed. It was no stranger to tears either, for it was refuge with its tall back and huge padded arms, and equally it was the platform that tiny feet bounced on when sheer joy needed to be given physical expression. Every house should have just such a chair.

Stories of Jeremy Giraffe, Waggertail and the Circus, and many such, consumed the hours that might otherwise have been spent dusting and polishing. Though if I had been a house proud Mum, we certainly wouldn't have kept the old chair, and I don't think any of my children would have forgiven me for that! Those wide-eyed expressions, and days of make-believe were the ones that memories are made of. And I have a lot of time for memories now.

Four years of fortnightly and lengthy visits to the hospital - lengthy because the journey had to be made by bus, and anyone who has lived in an English village in the sixties will recall how services rarely stretched to more than two buses a day, made inroads both on energy and the time one would normally have spent on the house. To arrive punctually often meant catching a bus two hours before the time of the appointment, and then trying to amuse three children in a busy town before there was a bus to bring us home. Whilst progress was being made, a day thus spent was time I would have given ten times over, but when the story was one of regression, my strength and energy were sapped.

CHAPTER ELEVEN

The boys were busily occupied with their wooden jigsaws one morning and I was making a weary attempt to catch up with the ironing. They had done them several times before, and were becoming sufficiently expert to challenge each other to races.

"I've only got four pieces left!"

"But mine's nearly done. Look Mummy I've finished first!" Despite my tiredness, their fun was infectious, and I suggested we switched on the oven timer.

"Right, let's see who can finish before the bell rings. Ready, steady, go!"

Their excitement made them noisier, and consequently less adept.

Minty, who until this time had been happily dosing Teddy, and One Eyed Doll with water medicine and smartie pills, was soon wanting to join in. I knew this was the point at which I ought to divert her. She would be eager to do a puzzle, and would fail. She would be miserable, and then it would be ages before she'd try again. I looked at the mountain of ironing; I must get some of it done. Perhaps she would be content just to watch the boys and clap her hands just as she always did when there was a race of any kind going on between them.

I recalled a conversation in the store earlier that morning. "Must rush dearie," benign old Alice had said, "It'll soon be wash-day and I still haven't finished last weeks ironing yet. Dunno where this week's gone to. Haven't been so behind in months."

Last week's ironing! I still had some of last *year's* in my basket! Horrid silky things that shrivelled when the iron was too hot; bits and pieces whose creases would not succumb because they should have been ironed when damp - only the opportunity to iron never came at the right moment. It wasn't the sort of thing you went around telling other people, but my ironing basket had never been completely empty since I'd had it. Well it was about time it was.

I spent far too much time doing the 'right' things with my offspring. And for what result? - a chaotic house whenever anyone called, endless uncompleted jobs, late night washing-up; a travesty of a garden and a reputation for being unsociable because I was never at coffee mornings. Minty had to have so much time, and because I loved them all equally, and couldn't bear them to think I didn't, the boys had to have extra stories and games too. And so it went on. But the ironing again - dammit I *would* empty that basket!

"Minty darling, give Teddy more medicine, and put dolly into bed." But she wasn't a nurse any longer; she wanted to do a puzzle. In fact she had already tipped a box full of pieces on the floor.

"Mummy - me make puzzle...me win. You help."

Her enthusiasm vied with her lack of co-ordination to produce in turn glee and frustration. After several minutes of mixing and turning, she forced two unmatching pieces to interlock and shrieked with delight, but when a third forced them into disarray, she surrendered to the difficulty and her hands hung limply.

"Puzzle no fit Mummy, you do it, you help."

"Yes Minty, just a few more seconds and I'll help." The iron sped over a couple more shirts, and then because she had given her attention to another toy, I carried on, simultaneously adding up the month's potential bills. She was quiet, and I thought, engrossed in a box of beads, until I noticed Neil looking sympathetically in her direction. She was silently weeping, a bit of chewed plywood puzzle in her sticky fingers.

"Oh Minty, I'm sorry. Come on we'll do the puzzle together. Let's find a nice bright one - look here's the circus one you like."

But the opportunity had faced me, and passed, and she was no longer interested. Oh why was there so much to do? Bob would be home soon and I hadn't given supper a thought.

"Mummy, Jon's cut his finger. Oh Mummy it's bleeding lots. Muu...my!" I tore to the kitchen where a potato peeler, the cause of the mutilation, was being held aloft by Neil. "Ooh look at all that blood! Mummy will he die?"

Bandaged and duly admonished, the victim recalled my attention to the deserted Minty. "Mummy, Minty's putting my puzzle out of the window, and Mummy it's raining."

"Oh no! Neil put on your raincoat and fetch Jon's puzzle. Heavens look at the time." Hastily I chopped onions and tomatoes, and shovelled some mince into the frying- pan. Shepherd's Pie again.

Eventually all was quiet, or as quiet as things ever are in a young family. The neat pile of ironing superciliously waited to be put away. And its price? A child who hated a puzzle so much that she had put it out of sight. Rather the same sentiment I now had for the ironing, and I dumped it unsorted into the airing cupboard. Avoiding toys that were way beyond her ability was vital, and yet so often impossible due her sustained determination to attempt whatever her brothers so excitedly performed, as if the attempt in itself proved her equality with them.

There had been a very brief period when a comparatively tranquil time had provided the opportunity to help her into achieving more than ever before. Neil, at two had been a fair competitor for her three and a half, whilst Jonathan a mere twelve months, someone to whom she could display accomplishments as yet beyond him....someone with whom she could commiserate when bricks fell down or trains ran off rails, assuring him that all would be well 'when he was big like her.' For six idyllically happy months, she was probably over achieving, and very much more assured in her new found confidence. Constant reassurance and encouragement were not so continuously required. She took the lead in deciding what game to play, and where in the garden to dig a hole. But of course, such a status quo could not last, and now with direct comparison within the family, the retardation that hitherto I had accepted with my head but never my heart, was forcibly brought home to me.

At last I could see what previously the outside world had seen and which my own emotions had blocked. The boys' eyes were bright with curiosity and wonder, whilst Minty's, though always kind and reflecting her immense capacity for loving, were much less sharp in their focusing, and somehow dimmer because of it. There were even days when I could see she wasn't pretty, and yes, at certain moments I had a fleeting glimpse of the bland ugliness of Jimmy McMahon, but an ugliness that was totally without meaning or impact now; for its very nature was transparent. In the way of looking at a beautiful garden without being aware of the window, so it is impossible to be in the company of such a child for very long before coming into contact with the gentleness of the soul beyond the physical features that encompass it.

The boys, at three and four were now strides ahead in physical and social development, and it seemed strange therefore that it was for Minty that school was being considered: an unorthodox concept that a child still in nappies would soon be ready for the outside world. Nevertheless it had become a frequent talking point when we were visited by doctors, health visitors and social workers.

Since our return, the State had displayed a commendable and ongoing awareness of our handicapped daughter; one that I appreciated and yet often found irritating because no-one ever made an appointment. Like most, we had no phone then, only a daily postal delivery. "I was just passing....thought I'd drop in to see your daughter", they'd say, as if we were lucky to be graced by an official's presence in the middle of washday.

Minty's file grew more complicated as various social workers called to observe, make notes, put forward opinions and pass judgement, and no more convince me they were interested in my girl or her condition, than the cat next door. It seemed to me that they were merely passing her along an assembly line, and as soon as she had passed through their own particular stretch of it, they filed her away. In fact, I suspected they came to pinpoint solely her degree of handicap in order to complete a required question on a form than to help her as a human being.

So many seemed hypocrites who took it upon themselves to tell me what was wrong with my child as if I had just purchased her as one would a second-hand car. They wore the badge of bureaucracy and considered it excluded them from the normal courtesies. Rightly or wrongly I found their intrusions an unbearable strain, and we decided therefore, to seek out the Medical Officer of Health for our area, and tell everyone else, as politely as possible, not to call again.

He proved to be a sensitive and charming man by the name of Blott who patiently explained the possibilities, and said that he would, if we were agreeable, come to the house to test Minty's ability in the familiarity of her own home. And, of course, we were. Minty warmed to him immediately and responded readily to his challenges with coloured counters and cards. There was something of Doc Cruickshank about him, though Dr Blott was taller, more distinguished, whose bearing carried the merest hint of 'success story'.

And so it should have done, for he was worthy of it. Tests over, he sat Minty on his knee, whilst suggesting to me that he should come and collect us whilst the boys were at nursery school one morning, so that we could visit a school some ten miles away that he thought might be appropriate for her.

It was such a treat to be chauffeur driven in a silent, luxurious car, and I was glad I'd put on my best two-piece. I wished the journey could have continued all morning for I hadn't felt so relaxed in ages. This was the sort of car afforded by many of the parents whose children attended the same nursery school as our two boys - a school run by a friend of mine, Nan, who had extracted a promise from me that if Minty went to school I would put in three mornings a week, on the basis of which, Neil and Jon were already installed.

She had recounted to me with some amusement, how, one morning when the children were seated at their tables having mid-morning milk, one little boy had, in a superior manner, grandly informed his table that it was Mummy' birthday and Daddy had given her a Lotus, no less. Of course, there had been cries of 'My mummy has a new mini...mine has blooo sports car'. Evidently, Jonathan having listened to all and sundry, with spectacle frames – no lenses - perched on the end of his nose, added dryly, "I bet you never had a van that broke down twice in one day!" For which comment, Nan informed me later, he was the envy of all! Cause for envy our van may have been, but this morning's ride made me feel pampered indeed.

"You're very quiet," Dr Blott commented, and I wondered whether to tell him about Jonathan's pride in our twelve-year-old van. But I didn't, and said I was a little apprehensive. He swung into the drive, parked expertly, and I knew we had reached another milestone.

In the large play area was an abundance of climbing frames, wheelbarrows, swings and cycles.

"They appear to be pretty well equipped," I said, remembering the last English school in which I'd taught.

"That's because these Centres are run by the Health Authorities and not your Education Department," he joked. "We are rather more affluent - though I couldn't begin to tell you why. Come on, I'll introduce you to Mrs Cadeby."

He had hardly voiced the words when the outer glass door was flung open, and a large, erect, and beaming woman greeted him warmly.

"I heard you in the drive - come into the office."

Dr Blott introduced me and her greeting was informal and welcoming. She indicated chairs, and we waited whilst she lit a cigarette, and I noticed how the doctor relaxed into the chair as she launched into the everyday happenings that had occurred since his last visit. He responded at intervals, but when the speed of her conversation became too enthusiastic for him to compete with, he smilingly fell silent.

After exuding for a full ten minutes, she acknowledged the fidgeting with his gloves, lit another cigarette and said good naturedly, "You know your way around; feel free." Dr Blott bowed slightly as she, resuming the conversation at breakneck speed, despite her previous comment, accompanied us to the first classroom. Windows occupied the whole of one side and overlooked a small play area exclusive to the kindergarten, whilst the room itself contained the type of play apparatus associated with nursery groups.

I was introduced to Miss Jones, a striking young woman, with dark hair elegantly drawn back into a French chignon. She was totally composed whilst surrounded by her demanding charges. She introduced Minty to the Wendy House and I was overtaken by a sense of panic as my daughter left my side to accompany her. Dr Blott placed a reassuring hand on my shoulder momentarily.

"Come and say hello to Mandy," he said, and I sensed that he wanted to prove to me that there is always someone worse off than oneself.

Stunned by the pathetic uselessness of the tiny, fragile body, I watched how Mandy's misty eyes stared unseeingly at her surroundings. Seemingly china hands dragged limply along the leather bound arms of her invalid carriage. Though a thick blanket covered her from the waist downwards, it was possible to tell from the contours made by her thighs and knees, that her limbs could give no support even to such a frail body. Dribble oozed from her mouth, and was mopped from her chin by adults I presumed to be Miss Jones' assistants, who performed the task as perfunctorily as a housewife would flick away dust.

I allowed myself to contemplate the enormity of this particular mistake of Nature, of the Great Force, or whatever other being was in charge of this unfair universe. Why was she allowed to be born? What tormenting force dragged her through each weary toneless day? Who was her mother and what did she think when she was alone? Did she want to screech at the Almighty to come out of his hiding place, to challenge Him to look her in the eye and justify all this....to explain how in his own Name he could perform miracles and yet allow this to happen.

People must have said all this about wars and famine and road accidents and unsuccessful operations, but in those cases, Man had a hand. Was this the result of God's infallibility? Where was the truth...non-existent or merely beyond the bounds of my comprehension?

Someone moved between me and the little girl, and I was aware of her as a disconnected shadow of Miss Jones... a new student perhaps, for she was not very sure of herself.

"Mrs Wade, would you wait over here now? It's time for prayers."

I gasped in disbelief. "You can ask that child to pray!"

There was a momentary uncomfortable silence. The shadow laughed patronisingly and with embarrassment.

"Oh but God didn't do it, did He?"

"Didn't He? No I suppose not." She winced at the bitterness of my tone. "I'm sorry, that was unfair of me." She couldn't have been more than seventeen.

"That's alright," she added. "I understand perfectly. It must be dreadful for you."

"No," I replied, "it's not dreadful, not in the way you think. No sympathy is needed. But please don't say you understand. After all, there's no reason why you should. You are still young enough to believe that tragedies only happen to other people. Deep down, you don't accept for one moment that any future child of yours could be handicapped." She recoiled again, and I hated myself for piercing her inexperience.

"That doesn't prevent me from understanding." She threw the words at me defiantly, for which I admired her, and began to arrange the chairs in a semicircle.

To myself I whispered, "Oh, but I'm afraid it does."

She clapped her hands to assemble the group. This was obviously a task assigned to her by Miss Jones, for I saw her nod in the student's direction. "Come along children, it's time to say thank-you."

Feeling nauseated, I retrieved Minty from the Wendy House. It was pointless to remain in this place. My little girl did not belong here. That she was retarded I had long since been convinced.....even mongol, if I said it quickly, but not like this...she would never resemble these scraps of humanity. To this quiet man who appeared already to have won her affection, I would have to say that she would never come here; that I was sorry to doubt his judgement, but that we must find somewhere else. And as I was thinking how to put it, he touched my arm and whispered, "I think we are in the way - shall we go to the next class?"

"Yes, of course," I said mechanically, and followed him down the corridor to see groups of children learning how to clean their shoes, sing nursery rhymes, cope with a spoon and fork, and to plant seeds. Pleasing sights in a nursery school, but this was not a nursery. Being short sighted, many of them brought their faces close to mine to examine more closely their reluctant visitor. Minty tugged on my hand as if eager to join them, but I held her close.

"Not these Minty - I'll find some other playmates for you."
Inside, my desperation was becoming near hysteria; only when the school bell rang at last did relief surge through me.

Dr Blott was an eternity saying Goodbye to the Headmistress, and when they finally shook hands, she beamed me an ample smile.

"Goodbye Mrs Wade. We'll be seeing you again, I hope."
I nodded but said only, "Thank you for letting me see your school: it was really kind of you."

I sank dispiritedly into the passenger seat of Dr Blott's car, totally drained. He didn't comment on our visit. Instead he told me of a 16-year-old girl who was on probation and whom he intended to visit that evening.

"What happened?"

"She did what I suppose I might do if I had nothing, and the rest of the world seemed to have so much. I wish I could get the magistrates to ask 'why?' rather more often than they seem to do."

"Perhaps they find that even when they ask why, it still doesn't alter what has happened."

He shot me a sidelong glance. "Are *you* still asking why?"

"Even after five years...yes I suppose I am."

"Mrs Cadeby's son died of leukaemia. I wonder if she continues to question?"

"You're not serious?" I gasped.

"I wouldn't joke about such a subject."

"But she looks so radiant and full of life."

"She decided that asking why, and sitting around waiting for answer eats up rather a lot of nervous energy that could be put to better use. Talking of energy, here are a couple of tickets for the show she's putting on next week."

"At the school?"

"Where else? That's her whole life. Don't come to any hard and fast decisions until you've seen it again."

"You're very perceptive." I smiled my thanks as we drew up to the gate.

"That was quite a painful two hours. Am I right?"

"Leukaemia must be worse," I replied, and closed the car door.

CHAPTER TWELVE

When I told Bob about the school he said it was like listening to a re-run of my account after visiting the little school in Canada.

"You mean I am back to square one as far as acceptance of it goes?" He didn't answer, and said that he ought to be getting some files ready for the trip to Paris tomorrow.

I reminded myself about Mrs Cadeby's refusal to worry about things she could do nothing about, but I was trapped in a circle of doubt and fear. How was it possible to be anything but depressed when thinking about little Mandy. I tried to be positive and recall the good things I had noticed; the modern kitchen where the older girls learned to cook, the sturdy toys and climbing frames...but over and above all these impressive inanimate objects were the groups of children who used them. Again, I could not convince myself that Minty could ever be like them; she often behaved so normally that no one would ever have guessed she was retarded. I was not to labour under this fallacy for very much longer!

The next morning she had an eye appointment at the hospital. We had been given the last appointment of the morning, and with each person running late, we were already one hour beyond our time. Minty and the boys were growing restless and I was on the point of telling yet another story when a doctor who had finished his clinic and who was obviously waiting for someone or something, came over in our direction. He tweaked the boys' noses and patted Minty.

"Hello girlie and who are you?"

Minty didn't answer. The boys filled in for her. "She's our sister!"

"My little girl is retarded," I explained.

He smiled gently. "Yes I see she is."

Feeling stupid for not guessing that that had been his reason for coming over, I could only ask, "How did you know?"

Poor man. I had placed him in an impossibly embarrassing situation, and it was quite evident he was thinking, 'Well it's obvious isn't it?'

"Does she look like other mongol children?" I asked weakly. "Are they really all the same?"

"Forgive me," he apologised. "I've been insensitive."

"Please be frank. You haven't answered my question."

"Well then, yes, they are all very similar aren't they?"

So that was what they mean by love being blind. He let her play with his tie. "I'm grateful to you," I said. Then the calling of Minty's name ended our stilted conversation and I sensed his relief.

"Will she soon be old enough to go to school?"

"Yes," I said taking a deep breath. "Very soon now."

On the way home Neil asked, "Mummy, what is mongol?"

I suppose it made a change from the usual questions for which parents prepare themselves. I was off guard and pretended to concentrate on the traffic. "Mummy I said what is...?"

"Yes sweetie, I heard you. Just wait while I get round this oil truck, and then we'll talk about it."

My mind searched for an answer. He wasn't capable of digesting biological facts but he now knew that his sister was different, and he needed to know why. I took as long as possible to manoeuvre the truck, by which time I had put together an answer.

"Close your eyes, and think about your nursery clock with its big hand and smaller one."

He squinted hard. "Yes."

"Can you remember what the little fat hand does whilst the long thin one rushes round the clock face?"

He grinned. "Yes it goes ever so slowly from number one to number two - so slowly you can never see it moving."

"That's right. Well suppose we call the long hand Neil, and the little one Minty. You see mongols are little boys and girls who take a long time to understand how to do things that you and Jon find easy."

It didn't seem a very adequate explanation, and I waited for his childlike demand for a better one, but instead he just snuggled closer, and was quiet all the way home. But as we all got out of the van he said, "But the little hand always gets there in the end, doesn't it Mummy?"

The childish words banished my depression and filled me with immense hope. His young mind had condensed the problem into something tangible, and his words had more impact than the similar, but more sophisticated ones Doc Cruickshank, and the London Ontario specialist had used, to tell me the same thing. We had a late lunch, and then I telephoned Dr Blott. "I just called to ask when there will be a vacancy at the school. I think perhaps Minty's almost ready."

"I'm glad you were pleased with what you saw," he said and it seemed pointless to say that I hadn't been, but that circumstances themselves presented no choice.

"It will be several months yet," he continued, and I thrilled to the sound of those words. I heard the pages of the diary being turned.

"Let's keep in mind November 1st as a possible starting date."

"November 1st," I repeated, and knew that the weeks up to that date would take on a jewel-like quality. I would make every one of them precious.

"Was there anything else Mrs Wade?" he interrupted my thoughts.

"Oh no, no. Except to thank you for taking me to the school." I replaced the receiver and knew I was no nearer to understanding it all than I had been five years ago. Not that my feelings hadn't changed; I no longer asked why it should have happened to me, because the fact was that it hadn't happened to *me;* it happened to Minty. She was the one that would have to toil around life's clock like the hour hand, so slowly, and always overtaken by others; she to whom many of life's pleasures would be denied. No longer did I see mongolism as a punishment for me: five years of having Minty had been mainly bliss. If I asked anything at all on my own behalf, it was what I had done to deserve her. But, as Dr Blott had noticed, I had not stopped asking what *she* had done to deserve being handicapped.

In all her young life there had never been a grumble or tantrum or disturbed night. Even her sad times evoked no aggression or recrimination. Putting the puzzle out of the window had not been done in swift anger, but rather a quite placid removal of something that for her, induced sadness, rather as one would have a pet put to sleep because he had uncharacteristically bitten the postman. She accepted whatever the day presented, and questioned nothing, and all the time exuded love and affection. But for *her* what was there?

Her friends would be those ugly little vegetables we had met at the school. She would never marry or have children of her own. By making her physically unattractive, nature was in fact taking great care not to reproduce its error, ascertaining that she would be one of the rejects on Love's roundabouts. It was all such a mystery, and all that I was certain of was that I loved her, and had grown to need her far more than perhaps she needed me as an individual. I could, I suspect, be replaced over a period of days in Minty's life, but I did not wish to suspect it, much less believe it. And now the first milestone was almost upon us. Minty was about to become a school girl.

It came as something of a shock therefore, when on one nightmare of an afternoon, some weeks later, a broad steely, insensitive female called at the house. She took two unblemished white forms from her folder, uncapped her expensive gold nibbed fountain pen, and peered over her glasses in the manner of a Ministry Official. "Let me see, er yes....name first."
I felt unwarrantedly pugilistic towards her and wanted to scream, "The same as it's been on all the other wretched forms we've filled in for your department. There must be a book of them by now.' But

instead, I just said coldly "Suzanne." And as her eyebrows shot up in question, I added "Minty's just a nickname."

"Yes of course." She smiled condescendingly. "And age?"

I could take no more.

"If after five years there is so little liaison within your department that you *still* find it necessary to ask me her name and her age, I really can see no point in my supplying it again."

Her expression registered annoyance, but she ignored my outburst and delved into the file, from which she was able to obtain Minty's date of birth and beautifully and painstakingly filled in the appropriate section of the form. Having done so, she produced a second sheet of paper and chose the moment to say reprimandingly, "Of course you'll want to do what's best for your child. Now if you would sign here saying that you agree she is uneducable within the education system..."

The blood drained from my face. This was officialdom gone mad. "I can't sign such a thing. No-one has ever suggested she is uneducable."

She fumbled amongst her file again.... "Oh, but you have already agreed she shouldn't go to school."

She was not listening and drew out another bit of paper and handed it to me. I was stunned as I saw my own signature dated a few days after my excursion with Dr Blott.

"That can't be right....we've already agreed a school. Dr Blott took me to it last month."

Efficient and cool again, she raised her eyebrows patronisingly.

"Ah, I see we don't quite understand. The school you visited is run by the Health Authorities and not the Ministry of Education. As far as the Education Authority is concerned, your child is technically uneducable, within mainstream education, of course."

She snapped her briefcase closed as if indicating she had finally penetrated my addled brain.

"Of course we both know that isn't strictly true, but she will need to be dealt with by the Health Authorities....now if you would just sign there....thank you. Well I think that concludes our little business."

She had dealt with the situation like the proverbial bull in a china shop!

A misty, chill November day - much the same as any other for the passers-by hurrying to catch the 8.30 bus into town - but for us, a milestone. At five and a bit, our little Minty was off to school. She was beaming brightly. She clearly understood what was about to happen and was so excited that we had made three frantic calls to the bathroom whilst waiting for the mini bus that would take her on her ten mile journey to the School for Retarded Children. She looked spruce in her new raincoat and gloves, and no-one would have suspected that her satchel contained not books and pencils, but a day's supply of nappies and rubber pants. She marched proudly up and down the drive, enthusiastically encouraged by the boys from the sitting-room window. Only her mother felt the world was falling to pieces!

Was this the beginning of the end of her attachment to us? I recalled what one social worker had said when suggesting we sent her into a residential home. 'She'll soon forget you: They very quickly attach themselves to those who look after them.' I shuddered involuntarily. God forbid. I looked down the road and waved to the driver of the bus who was obviously searching for our house.

She bounded onto the bus as if it were the greatest adventure of all time; assured and deliriously happy, she settled herself in ladylike fashion on the front seat. The world was her oyster. She had tasted independence, and loved it. Jauntily, she waved goodbye and the bus-guide told me not to worry. I nodded, not daring to risk my voice.

The little bus pulled away, and its motley crew of smilingly complacent passengers all grinned and waved. I responded until they disappeared from view but once inside I gave way to the feelings that had been building up over the past few weeks. I cried like a baby, and the tears rolled down my cheeks uncontrollably.

The house was a mess. Despite the fact I had been up since 6 a.m. I had been able to concentrate on nothing but getting Minty off to school. The sink was a shamble of dirty dishes, and every work top a clutter of breakfast packets and eggshells. An hour later saw little progress.

I have not experienced many interminably long days, but Minty's first day at school was surely one of the longest I have ever lived through. That afternoon saw me standing on the corner of the lane long before the bus was due. The air was damp and cold, and in my eagerness to see her again, I had come out without a coat.

At last the minibus came into view just beyond the bend by the local pub. An empty day had come to an end; Minty was home again. As the bus drew level, such a sorrowful little face peered at me from the window, and as she was lifted down to me I felt the tiredness in her.

"Mummy," she whispered. "Me home. No school." So many tears from one tiny exhausted girl.

She ate no tea, and refused to leave my side. Falling asleep before Bob came home, she crumbled into her bed, her breathing still uneven from the hours of misery. I stayed until she was fast asleep and then went downstairs to prepare supper.

"Hi Minty," Bob called as he came down the drive. "How was school little lady?" Then blankly, as he entered the kitchen and still no bear hug. "Where is she?"

"Gone to sleep," proffered Jonathan, "cos she didn't like school."

"Very miserable?" and I nodded. "She's shed a bucketful of tears and brought home three wet nappies."

Dejectedly we ate our meal, and then I did some mending whilst Bob wrote a couple of letters and suggested an early night. "Poor little mite. Wonder how long it will take?"

The answer was three months. She would waken us at six o'clock with a plaintive little voice. "No school today. Me holiday." The crying actually stopped after several weeks, but the white, sadly pleading face that followed was even harder to bear, and the abandonment in her eyes each morning as I handed her into the care of the bus guide was sheer torment.

Each morning I vowed it would be for the last time; what was the point of continuing? Of course, for almost every child, the novelty of school wears off after a week or so, but Minty had been desolate for three months now. Yet each time I decided to phone Dr Blott, I remembered Dr Cruickshank's words 'Remember it may take your wee one months, or even years, to do what the lucky ones do in weeks'. I had interpreted his words to mean walking and feeding herself, or becoming dry. Surely he couldn't have meant she could go on hating school for years?

In the absence of comforting thought, I wondered if a stiff brandy could be as effective in real life as in films. It was amazing we had any in the house, but Christmas was only two months past, and I was able to indulge. At least I was almost able to. Just as I was on the point of pouring, Betty, a friend in the village who was beyond the stage of knocking at the door, came into the kitchen.

"Helen, I've got some news..." And then, seeing the brandy bottle, she stopped, her mouth falling open. Wedged between the washing machine and the oven, glass in one hand, and half empty brandy bottle in the other at 8.45 on a Monday morning, I realised that to satisfy the agog Betty, I had some pretty sharp explaining-to do.

"Caught in the act," I said, not really feeling jocular.

"Looks a bit like it."

I thought Betty seemed unduly concerned. "How long has this been going on?"

"Oh I shouldn't think there is much hope for me now. Strange you've never noticed it before. Oh Betty for heavens sake... I reached for another glass. Join me and we can look debauched together."

"Oh no I mustn't. That's what I've come to tell you." She could not contain her excitement for she had waited a long time for a baby. "Stuart's like a dog with two tails."

Her husband had refused to consider adoption that had caused a degree of bitterness in their marriage. "Of course; we won't be telling anyone for three months."

"Thanks for the compliment," I grinned, and meant it. "I won't breathe a word. Sure you won't have some? Just a drop can't harm."

"I will if you tell me why you're feeling the need of it," she answered.

"Half medicinal; half psychological. They do it in all the best films."

"What's the problem? Overdoing it?"

I told her about Minty, and confessed I didn't know what to do about her. She suddenly seemed to sit on the stool more firmly.

"Helen," and then a pause, "Minty isn't the only one who is looking distressed lately. We have all noticed. Couldn't you reconsider the idea of her going to boarding school?"

"In nine months time you'll have more sense than to ask such a daft question."

"Now I've upset you. I should have known."

"Yes I suppose you have a bit. Be an angel, and don't make suggestions like that again."

"O.K. but it wasn't a daft notion. I've thought about it a lot this past week, and I know I couldn't keep a mongol baby."

"I'm sorry Minty has made you feel like that," I said testily. "I happen to think she's rather wonderful."

"Helen, we all do. She's doing amazingly well. Oh let's forget it."

"Good idea," I agreed, feeling ashamed of my reaction. "Come and see the fancy dress I've concocted for the kids."

She picked up the Bill and Ben outfits I had made for the boys. I had had difficulty in restraining them from a trial run that morning as I had little faith in the costumes' durability beyond the half-hour allocated for the parade.

"What a tremendous pair," she enthused.

"Threesome," I corrected her.

The boys wouldn't leave Minty out and she was to go as Weed. I held up the silk convolvulus I was pinning to her white dress.

"I'll be rooting for them," she promised, grinning at the unintended pun.

"Thanks. Now drag up a stool and chat to me over the soapsuds. What do you want - a boy or a girl?"

"Either, just so long as it's..."

"Normal," I finished for her. "Of course... don't look uncomfortable. That's what everybody wants."

"Helen, tell me something, though I've no right to ask... Did you ever wish Minty had died?"

"Yes, because I never thought she could ever achieve any happiness. I suppose without thinking about it, I believed she understood her condition as we did, and would resent it. And, of course, that's not true. Nor did I think she could ever cope with the hurt others would inflict on her because she was different... Most of all, neither Bob nor I had belief in our power to make her happy, or to compensate her for the rotten start she has had."

"I've never seen it that way. I've always thought of it as your ill fortune."

"I think that's the way most people see it, but only because Minty is too young for them to have had any interaction with her."

We chatted intermittently whilst I took baskets of wet washing outside and then made sandwiches. It was mid afternoon before she eventually left. Her presence, for which I was grateful, had swallowed up most of the day.

And then the break came. By the afternoon post, a small package arrived from the hospital together with a note requesting Minty entered the ward for another cataract operation. Her right eye had become very cloudy of late, and it had occurred to me more than once that her restricted vision might be the cause of feeling so insecure at school. Perhaps a period in hospital would provide the watershed she needed before attempting school again. Anything at all that broke the continual misery, would be a godsend.

And so it was with a lighter heart that I met the school bus that day. But to my amazement a much happier daughter greeted me. In her paint-stained hand she clutched a grubby, and many times folded piece of paper.

"Me do it. Me paint!" We ran inside where, responding to my own enthusiasm, she opened up the work of art. And I could not have been prouder if she had won a scholarship to the Royal Academy. My intelligence told me that it was a large red splodge next to a smaller blue one, with lots of purple trickles where the two colours had run into each other. But who, in such circumstances relies on intelligence? Here was a masterpiece! Prodigious talent! I hugged her, and we jumped up and down. The boys laughed infectiously and patted her on the back with shrieks of 'Clever Minty', as we ceremoniously taped it to the kitchen wall where its unquestioned magnificence lent grandeur to the pots and pans and scales. Most marvellous of all, Minty was bursting with the joy of achievement.

"Me go school again tomorrow!" she announced.

We got round it somehow; I think the promise that the boys and I would go shopping for some new paints and brushes was greatly instrumental! Whilst Neil and Jon were noisily putting her mind at rest on the subject of being away from home, (something of course they hadn't yet done), she sat benignly, and a little self-importantly on her stool, graciously accepting all their offers and promises. And when they finally ran out of suggestions on 'How to stay happy in hospital', she unclasped her hands, stretched her toes to reach the floor, and announced that she would go to pack her case - and would the boys like to help?

I think even they were taken aback by her placid acceptance of the situation, so much so that they could think of no objection to lending grubby hands. Minty had not yet developed the ability, and seemed not to have the imagination to project herself forward into a new situation. Of course, she had been in hospital before, but at such a young age she did not remember it. Whereas the boys at three and

119

four decided an operation was rotten luck, their sister was, at this point in time, warm and secure in familiar surroundings, and could feel none of the awe and anxiety or excitement evident in Neil's comments since hearing the news. She had reached only the stage of projecting herself into known situations, and had not mentally noted that going into hospital would involve many of the things she found so unbearable about going to School.

Bob and I talked late into the night about the chances of success this time, though we had both grown as confident of the surgeon who constantly kept a check on her, as Minty had grown fond of him. If anyone could improve her sight, then he could.

When packing her case, I included bits and pieces wrapped in brightly coloured paper. There were few things Minty enjoyed more than unwrapping parcels, and I hoped they would pass some of the time spent in preparing for the operation.

We arrived late, grubby and hot after a snapped fan belt delayed us by an hour and a half, and were just in time to prevent Sister telephoning another family to offer Minty's bed that was in a small, side ward containing one other little girl, who at this stage was too shy to do more than watch us guardedly from behind the bars of her cot.

Up to the day of the operation, the boys were allowed to visit with me. Periodically, I would take them out to the park nearby to run off some energy, and then on our return to buy a cup of tea and biscuit at the W.V.S. Unit in the Out-Patients Department, and the inevitable chat with Mrs Partridge. The next day was spent in similar fashion, the two boys 'helping' the nurse to put drops in Minty's eyes.

Occasionally we would visit some of the elderly patients in the larger ward to which Minty's was attached. Old age, in taking away so much, brought with it, abundant tolerance and understanding. Never has a hurtful glance or sharp word emanated from an old man or woman on the subject of retardation, in my experience. Perhaps, because of their enforced slowness, they are themselves the more patient to wait for a little tortoise-girl, as Jonathan often described his sister... and certainly they seemed overjoyed when they were visited by youngsters encouraged to say a few shy words.

On the third day we were not allowed to visit at all. This was D-Day, and although the needling took little more than a few minutes, Minty would spend the day quietly, with eyes padded and bandaged. We were to phone later that evening for news.

Trying desperately not to hope for too much is contrary to human nature. Several years ago, three successive operations had been necessary before success had been achieved and even so, more cataracts had now developed and it was necessary for Mr Paton to start all over again. As we walked to the call-box down the lane that evening, assuring each other that it was bound to be alright, we each warned ourselves that it may not be.

But it was! And Bob was hugging me before he could put the receiver down. We fairly bounded home, throwing ourselves into the kitchen, but suppressing our first instinct to dash upstairs to tell the boys. They were too young to be given any idea that things might ever be less than successful in hospital. We put away two sizzling hot plates of eggs and bacon, and spent the evening doing absolutely nothing other than to feel that life was pretty good.

Three of us journeyed into the town on the lunchtime bus next day, and walked through the park to the hospital. To my horror, when I opened the door of the side ward, there was no Minty; only a neatly made white bed, and on the opposite side of the room, a sleeping Sarah. Trying to conceal my anxiety from the boys, I knocked tensely on the door of Sister's office. "Sister, where...?" And then the relief as I witnessed such an amusing sight. Minty, sedately seated on an upturned totty-pot, was reading 'Three Bears' from a medical dictionary. Sister had a thermometer under her arm, and one leg propped up on the spare chair. Minty greeted us without surprise, but said seriously, "Ssh, Sister very ill!"

"Ill or not young lady, I'm going to hand you over to your Mum before I'm fired."

There was a general all round hugging, and the inevitable question,

"How much can she see?"

"It's difficult to say yet. She has ointment in her eyes of course, and the eye will take a few days to settle down, but Mr Paton is very pleased. He'll be coming round again this afternoon to see her."

My thanks were inadequate, but I think Sister understood.

"She's fun to have around," she said.

It was seldom that anyone remarked on the positive side of her nature, and I was a little taken aback, "I'm glad she's been no bother."

"Oh I didn't say that!" she smiled wryly. "She's been an absolute scamp. Every time I turn round something's missing."

It was sheer joy to be discussing Minty in normal terms, instead of being the recipient of sympathy and kind understanding. That she was seen to have her share of mischief and ability to be a nuisance, filled me with nothing but pride.

It was only two days before she was home again, a brighter, chirpier, and better-able-to-see child. She became almost confident, and we were regaled with pigeon-English descriptions of doctors, nurses and cleaners who dropped water jugs and bedpans, seemingly incessantly! And just for good measure she had picked up a couple of swear words! The confidence she had gained in hospital was never lost. Someone must have recognised that there were to be many more such periods of hospitalisation for her in the future, and understood the importance of avoiding all fear and trepidation of having to stay away from home for treatment.

It had its effect on her return to school too, and the tears at last were at an end, and she began to enjoy life to the full. She loved nothing more than to mimic her friends and her teachers for our entertainment. Because her recollections were completely photogenic as opposed to intelligent, she achieved a much less inhibited performance than she might otherwise have done. We all rolled with laughter as she became 'teacher', crossed her legs and adjusted her skirt, and pronounced regally that Jonathan had dirty knees and must go and wash immediately with lots of soap!

It was at times like those that we wondered whether being normal was really all that marvellous. Were people happier for being normal? Now that she was confidently installed in school, it didn't seem possible for anyone to be more content than she. And wasn't happiness what every parent wanted for their children? Success, yes. Security and a sound future. But happiness most of all. And would being normal automatically mean that life was good. If she *were* able to marry, was there any guarantee that her husband wouldn't turn out to be a swine? Supposing she had an exceptional brain: might she be so highly strung that exams threw her into a state of suicide? What had normality really to offer over and above the security she had now, and would always have, of being cared for by those who loved her. She would never know the worry of coping with the bills, or the stress of day-to-day living; she need never be part of the rat race or dog-eat-dog society that seemed to be threatening. The smiles, the spontaneous loving, the utter faith in us, her family, enriched all our lives.

Bob and I frequently discussed the possibility that if anyone might suffer at some time because of Minty's condition, then it could be our boys, who, though having had mongolism explained, were still much too young to realise all the implications. As yet they inevitably turned to their sister for comfort and solace if miserable; she happily placated and adored them, fetching and carrying for them for the sheer pleasure it gave her to be needed. The strength of the bond between them was evident in a thousand different ways. But would it always be so? Would they, as teenagers, still bring their friends to tea or would having a retarded sister embarrass them? Worst of all to contemplate was the possibility that a girlfriend might refuse to marry rather than risk a similarly afflicted child.

The fear did not seem stupid then, for despite the beginnings of progress in this field of medical science, the attitude of many people to the mentally handicapped remained almost Victorian. Now, some thirty odd years later, though it may contain more vandals, increasing violence; though old ladies fear for their safety in their own homes, the world is kinder in its attitude to the handicapped. People like Minty are not called mongol any more, but the gentler sounding Down's Syndrome. Though she suffered the indignity of pointed fingers many times as a child, now there is a tolerance and understanding that I would not have dreamed of even ten years ago. And as for the fear of producing a mentally handicapped baby, tests can reveal this very soon after conception and no young couple needs to give birth to a 'Minty' baby.

Whatever else has deteriorated in this modern world, there is a greater awareness, compassion and acceptance of the hitherto 'strange' ones. Not so when she was a child, and we were to be reminded of this when, some months later, Bob came to find me in the garden where I was tidying the borders.

"Helen, Tom's on the phone..."

"Oh the baby! What is it? Girl? Boy?..."

His look told me that the sex didn't matter: there were other more important things, such as life itself for instance.

"Bob, what's wrong?"

"Tom wants you to go and be with Betty for awhile. I'll drive you to the hospital, and bring him back here. Only we'll have to take Minty..."

"Well why not? She knows Tom...Oh you don't mean..."

He nodded and our minds raced back in tandem to a snow-laden night in Canada.

"I'll take the van," I said mechanically. "Tom will have theirs at the hospital and it's the children's bedtime anyway."

Betty was lying in bed staring at the ceiling, and studiously avoiding the baby in the crib by her side.

"It'll be alright Bet. I promise. Only I can't explain now." I was angry at my inadequacy. All the way there I had planned what I would say, but seeing her was to experience a replay of the hours I had lived through after Doc Cruickshank had broken the news to *us*.

She looked at me imploringly, as if needing me to utter something profound, or to let her in to a closely guarded secret.

"I'll never love him as you love Minty, Helen. Never! I don't know how I'll ever love him at all."

"Don't you remember how I told you how I wished Minty would die?" I was glad that I had told her that day in the kitchen, and not now, tonight. "Anyway, you'll be amazed when you find you don't even have to try to love him. You've a hell of a nice surprise in store."

She shook her head disbelievingly, as I knew she would, and as I remembered I had done, and the only reason I went on talking was that I was part of the process of passing the minutes of that eternity of a first night of knowing.

"Everyone in the village said they didn't know how you did it, and Helen, I agreed with them." She continued to gaze at the ceiling.

"That's because until tonight you were one of them." Momentarily, I felt a surge of anger as I realised how patronising 'they' had been if they had felt like that, and yet said nice things to us when we met in the street.

"You are in the club now, and you'll see it differently after awhile."

"A club I don't remember asking to join," she returned bitterly.

"I don't think any of its members did that Betty. I hardly recall filling in an application form myself."

She ignored my comment and wept, "Oh God after all these years of waiting." She did not realise the impossibility of what she had asked of me, for I was meant to have come as a friend who could supply all the answers and somehow take the hurt away, and it was all I could do to hide the fact that I was sharing the wretchedness that now enveloped her.

"Helen, look at him, and tell me they've made a mistake. Tell me they've got it all wrong. Doctors are not infallible..."

I was already saying the words with her, for had I not learned the same part several years ago?

I gazed at the little mass of protoplasm that lay beneath such mockingly dainty nylon. Inexplicably he suddenly became the only person in the room. I slid my finger in his hand. Silently and stupidly I talked to him, as if he had already been hurt by our comments.

'She's stunned right now and doesn't understand how much you are going to need her; she thinks she won't cope. It is incomprehensible to her that you can possibly ever do more than lie there. She sees you as an inert, ungenerous and demanding catastrophe. And it is only the catastrophe for which she can feel - not you yourself, because she believes you have no personality. She's afraid that you'll test her limits of mental and physical endurance, and find her wanting; that you will sap every ounce of energy she can produce, every scrap of patience and perception she can find within her. She thinks you will do all the taking... more than she is prepared to give, because you see, she doesn't know you yet. You haven't had a chance to show her how, in this cruel world, you'll need someone to guard you against the prying, curious eye, the ridicule from the ignorant, and the condescending comments from the lucky ones.

Be patient, ugly duckling, while she comes to terms with all this, and learns how, in return for caring for you, you'll give her such unconditional, and overwhelmingly wholesome love, and moments of such sheer delight, she'll want to make time stop forever. You'll endow her with the ability to retain her faith in human nature against all possible odds. For her, if for her only, you will become a beautiful swan, and make her feel the most selfish and indulged of women under the weight of all your giving; and your need of her will draw you together in an indestructible bond forever.'

He snuggled his cheek closer to the warmth of the pillow, and his tiny hand remained closed around my fingers.

'Be patient little Tom junior - perhaps for a long time because she can't see yet through the dense disappointment of hurt. She certainly can't see further than your funny face, little chap. You're not very handsome are you? You'd look a lot better without those frills and lace all round you. Your poor Mum and Dad were expecting a princess you see...'

"You've been looking at him a long time Helen."

I released my hand from her baby and transferred it to hers.

"They haven't made a mistake Betty. Have a good weep. Shout if you like: it'll help to release your feelings."

"Don't be daft," she said, "I'll wake all the babies up."

"Ah, but this one's special. *He'll* forgive you."

The tears flowed freely - hers and mine - until the nurse came to give her something to help her sleep.

She was drained of all the hope and eagerness with which she had awaited this baby. I searched for words that would do more than sympathise. In the years to come, she would read all manner of print relating to retardation: even in the next few weeks there would be pamphlets issued to tell her that it was perhaps understandable, but not reasonable to feel she was to blame; that if she and Tom felt inadequate to the demands, they must not entertain a guilt complex. Health visitors would call, painfully to extract trivia to be recorded that they might be of assistance when the child grew up a little. But what help was there *now,* in these first hours of knowing, of being told, 'Mother, your baby is mentally handicapped.' The sleeping pill could only delay the agony.

The years for Betty and Tom, and us, passed; slowly at first, and then gained momentum as the children went to school. Teachers were then at a premium, and I received an increasing number of requests to respond to the many posters all around the town, to return to teaching. Headmasters resorted to knocking at the front door, and so desperate was one that he called to collect me each day for the duration of a permanent teacher's illness, because we did not boast a second car.

I enjoyed being a professional woman again, even more so because it relieved the tension on our finances. When a friend told me there was an opening at a school four miles away, I readily agreed to an interview. Minty's bus, that collected her from home at 9.a.m., actually picked up another child outside the particular school at 8.45. As the Head was apparently desperate for staff, he could surely have no objection to her accompanying me whilst I prepared the classroom for the day's work, before slipping out to put her on the coach prior to the children's arrival.

But I was wrong. He read my references, offered me the job, and then when I explained the situation, promptly withdrew the offer. He couldn't possibly contemplate such an arrangement.

"Have you ever thought of boarding school?"

Without waiting for my reply he added, "I don't speak without experience of the subject. A cousin of mine - a canon as a matter of fact - had such a child."

He said this with a pompous indignation I'd often heard before, as if someone had played a rather vulgar joke in allowing a handicapped child to be born to a canon.

"You know it gets worse as time goes by. They slow up considerably. This child - my cousin's girl was quite friendly as a youngster, but it got to the stage where she wouldn't be with anyone but her nanny. People like me, who could have taken her out for a walk, she'd have nothing to do with. Completely unsociable."

He halted as if waiting for an interjection from me. "Well, er, my advice to you is to think it over very, very carefully."

"I have," I replied. "Probably more carefully than you could imagine. And there is no question of her being sent away. And if I may say so, Mr Harries, you would undoubtedly have fewer lines on your forehead if you hadn't taken on the task of running this school. You'd be less tired if you could be rid of the niggling hassle of being Headmaster. But you would rightly think mad anyone who suggested that you throw it all up and pass the responsibility to someone else. You couldn't pull out if you had a South Sea Island handed to you free for the rest of you life, for the simple reason you have put too much of yourself into it."

"Mrs Wade, I haven't invited you here today to lecture me on my position as Head."

My hackles were up. "And nor have I come to you to be questioned on my right to bring up my own child. And since you took the liberty of deciding Minty would be better off in a boarding school without ever having seen her, may I take a similar liberty, and guess, that without ever having seen your cousin's daughter, the reason she wouldn't go for a walk with you was that she knew you didn't really want to take her... handicapped children have few real friends, but make no mistake, they know acutely who those friends are. They don't possess the finesse and tact to avoid the company of the insincere; they just quietly rebuff."

"I find your manner offensive. I was never insincere. I cared very deeply about my cousin's plight."

"Your cousin's plight - yes. Don't you see, that's why you couldn't get near to her. You regarded her as the tragedy that had happened to your cousin. If only you could have considered the handicap as the tragedy that happened to *her*. But you felt as hopelessly ineffective as if she were behind bars."

"How can you presume to know how I felt?"

"Because I felt all these things, and still do with many handicapped children. When I can't find them appealing, it's better to be honest and stay away." I regretted sounding so righteous, and admitted, "Only sometimes its impossible to remain aloof, as I'm sure you know: circumstances don't allow it, and then it's awful. I'm sorry."

My rudeness having talked me out of a job, I apologised and said goodbye.

"You're on the inside, and I expect that makes a difference," he conceded, and I had the distinct feeling that if we had been able to talk a little longer, we may have become friends. He rang the bell to summon the next applicant.

Another Head took a diametrically opposed view, even though, by the time the bus passed *his* school, it was often after 9.00 a.m.

"Bring her in, and let the children take turns at escorting her to the coach. Tell the driver he can pull into the gateway. Your girl will enjoy the company and they will be better people for the contact with her. That little exercise in human relationships will do them more good than my assemblies. They won't take so much for granted either. Can you start tomorrow - both of you?"

We did, and so started a blissfully uneventful year in which we had time to live less demanding and exacting lives, for Mr Paton had now done all he could for Minty's eyesight.

CHAPTER   THIRTEEN

Not long afterwards we began what we with hindsight called 'our overseas period' Our first sojourn overseas was a result of Bob's frustration with the management of the Chemical plant where he worked, for having lived abroad he was finding the U.K. restrictive. He joined an international company and our first tour was the most colourful and memorable of all, Thailand, where Minty at seven was accepted unequivocally into the Reception Class of the Bangkok Patana School.

The staff were mainly Australian and New Zealanders who explained that they had no policy of 'special schools', and that all children were absorbed into the mainstream educational system. Minty's growth, as well as her mental development being retarded, she fitted in beautifully with children only two years her junior and commenced what was to prove one of the happiest periods of her life, as far as companionship and achievement were concerned.

As indeed did the boys. All three children were fascinated by their classrooms that were built on stilts, with awnings of bamboo and 'walls' of flimsy three ft. high lap-fencing. Thus any precious breeze could pass through the structures unimpeded. The one door in each prevented the entry of any reptile that took it upon itself to mount the four steep wooden steps the children climbed each day.

No sooner were Minty, Neil and Jon accepted onto the roll, than the headmistress, a lithe and wiry fifty year old who, though English born, had been educated and brought up in South Africa, asked if I would become a supply teacher. I was delighted to agree for I did not feel comfortable sharing my home with servants I did not know and who barefoot and silently seemed forever to appear from nowhere. By virtue of being installed before I arrived, they gave the impression of feeling much safer about their position than I did. Indeed, I did not enjoy being waited on and addressed as Madame, and found it well nigh impossible to instruct them to fetch and carry for me, though unless one did, there appeared to be no inclination to volunteer, except in the case of Pan the gardener, who was always willing to offer to help with anything if it meant he did not have to be in the garden!

We noticed our Thai neighbours certainly experienced no such difficulty with their staff when they invited us round for cocktails one evening shortly after the children and I arrived, Bob having left the U.K. a month prior in order to locate a house and staff. As soon as one of their servants entered the room, she would drop to the floor and approach her master or mistress on her knees. When drinks were offered to us in like fashion, my instinct was to gesture to the girl that this was unnecessary, but I saw a swift flash of anger cross my hostess' face before the inscrutable smile was replaced, and I resisted the impulse.

But now here was someone not only offering me the opportunity to teach, but to have a reason to leave the domestic scene immediately after breakfast.

"Call on me whenever you like," I said gratefully, handing her my phone number.

"I'm calling now," she laughed. "I've got a teacher who has been delayed at the border... she and her friend went off to Chengmai for the long weekend. These youngsters can't seem to get it into their heads that this is not Europe where they can hitch a lift in safety. Look, why not stay and have a cool drink, let the children go and meet their classmates, and you begin formally tomorrow."

"You mean you don't expect her back then?"

"Most unlikely. She'll learn."

In less than a month I had a class of my own, for here the staff were, in the main, married to husbands in business, whose tours of duty did not begin and end to fit in neatly with school terms. I learned that the school was begun some fifteen years earlier by a group of parents who did not wish to leave their offspring at boarding school in the U.K. at the tender age of five. Two of the group were teachers, and from a base of one Infant and one Junior class, the school grew to the fourteen class establishment of which we now became a part.

I have never enjoyed teaching anywhere so much. The children in my class came from all over the world, though each had at least one English-speaking parent, and the interaction of backgrounds was continually stimulating.

It was my first encounter with the 'Aussie' approach to life, and though discipline was tight, and standards of achievement maintained at a high level, so there was a lively emphasis on fun and simply being glad to be alive. Most noticeably there was a total lack of pettiness. A cheerful willingness to get on with whatever conditions presented themselves, ensured a tolerant and sociable staff. They made a newcomer welcome, but there was no question of being carried. One learned to cope, or to accept that sinking was the only alternative.

School began briskly at 7.30 a.m. and ended at mid day when the heat and humidity became nigh unbearable. We would amble listlessly homewards, the unrelenting sun beating down on us, our eyes dazzled by its sheer brilliance. We could feel the heat from the rough concrete road through our flip-flops that made a tacky sound with each step forward. Like a little animal seeking the shade, Minty would go straight to her room, lie quite still on her bed protected by her mosquito net, and gain what comfort she could from the movement of air by a fan suspended from the ceiling - the nearest the house could boast in the way of air conditioning. Not for her to trail the buffalo or feed the bad tempered geese on the klong that flowed lethargically through our garden. She was happy to leave such debilitating pursuits to her brothers, for whom Thailand was an absorbing new world.

The accepted format for 'expats' was for wives and children to merge at the British Club for the afternoon after a midday siesta, and to enjoy elegantly served tea around an inviting pool. Husbands would arrive after their day in air conditioned offices at around 5.30, partake of a swim and a cocktail, before the whole family returned either to be served dinner at home, or more usually for the children to eat and go to bed whilst parents, having the luxury of baby sitters 'in situ' would dine out or attend cocktail parties. An artificial life; indeed very enjoyable for a while, and many days saw us doing just that.

But I wanted to know the local and *real* Thailand, and sometimes asked one of the girls who looked after the house and would be only too willing for an excursion, to accompany me to the markets and shops that *they* frequented. It did not take long to discover that in these markets, food was a quarter of the price of produce in markets patronised by more senior servants working for American personnel. Always we came home laden with fruit, and now and then anything from a baby duckling to a new spice. We spent many a fascinating afternoon watching craftsmen working on wood turned bowls and the creation of bronze cutlery, not to mention 'priceless' gems being polished from Coca-Cola bottles!

"You mean you allow people to think they are buying valuable jewellery?" I asked incredulously on one occasion.

"Can Madam tell the difference?" a charming Thai of about fifty asked me.

"That's exactly what I mean - I *can't* tell the difference."

"Beauty is in the eye of the beholder, Madam. If a gentleman thinks he gives his mistress a rare and beautiful stone, then the stone assumes that quality. Who am I to deprive him of that pleasure?"

"Or his money," I smiled.

"I do not force him to give me his money. I merely display my goods."

It was quite incongruous to think there might have been a Thai equivalent of the Trades Description Act! The fact of a card bearing the words 'precious stones' was immaterial!

"Is not your little girl precious? But to another, a child to be avoided," he said with practical honesty. "How do you value what is precious?"

I learned a lot about Oriental philosophy during those trips. He was not being dishonest within his own culture. If purchasers were stupid or ignorant then any outcome must be their misfortune. Trust was something to be earned, not given automatically.

Most of all the children loved to sit inside the tailors' shops. The Chinese were the quickest and most efficient, and worked such long hours. One could order a gentleman's dress shirt, and it would be ready within the hour; a new suit completed in an afternoon. The whirring of the sewing machines and the earnest dexterity of the tailors never failed to hold their attention - or mine.

I noticed that the Thais seemed always to want to place a hand on Minty's head as they passed her in the street. Though at first she was a little nonplussed by the constant attention she received, she soon grew less shy, and thinking this was a Thai greeting, reciprocated by reaching up to place *both* her hands on the heads of those who were more familiar to her. The young girls giggled, for beyond a dozen words, we were unable to speak to each other, whilst older women reached out and invited her to squat on the pavement with them, and she, fascinated by the number and colour of the flip-flops costing only a few baht a pair, would readily oblige. I suspect she 'lost' more than one in the klong just so as to go and buy some new ones.

Strange too that while burglary was so commonplace, in all the time we were there we had no direct experience of it. I endeavoured to discover the reason, and did not bargain for the reply:

1.	Little Miss Minty lived in the house;
2.	The house was haunted!

Which was the greater deterrent, I never learned! But at least the second reason was somewhat comforting in that it accounted for our high turnover of staff. The departure of so many had left me perplexed, for we believed we were not nearly so demanding as many who suddenly found themselves with servants for the first time.

We fell over backwards to see they had adequate time off, which in itself was a mistake for we were then assumed to be a 'soft touch,' and the stealing - of which there had always been a certain amount and to which we were advised to turn a blind eye - escalated to a ridiculous level.

"But we just did not eat 40lbs of sugar in one month," I remonstrated with Suan, but she continued to pare her nails disinterestedly, using the long sharp knife she, like most of the girls, kept under her pillow at night. And the bland smile disclaimed all understanding of English, despite the sugar packet in my hands. She had been the only wash-girl to disregard the monks' claim that the house was haunted, and the only one I longed to see the back of.

Money too began to disappear, and it was discomforting to say the least, not to be able to put money down in our own home. Bewildering too, for the girls, once the cleaning had been completed, did not enter anywhere but the kitchen and dining room for the rest of the day. There were no pockets in their long wrap-around skirts, nor did their hands ever appear to be telltale clenched.

Quite by accident one day, we solved the mystery. All three children were immensely fond of Pan, the houseboy and gardener, who, at seventeen, aspired to a more ambitious lifestyle than domestic service, and asked in virtual sign language if we would teach him to speak 'American'. The word English did not feature in his vocabulary for his knowledge of the outside world began and ended with the Vietnam War which was then in progress, and it was to Bangkok that American servicemen were sent for rest and recuperation, in the form of hundreds of dollars to be spent in one long weekend. Thus it was that scores of pretty Thai girls were liberated from lowly paid domestic service by accepting jobs in nightclubs, bars and massage parlours. Pan's sister was one of them.

By being with Minty, Neil and Jon, he picked up a great deal, not least of all by listening to the boys urging Minty to speak clearly. The repetition they induced from her served also to increase Pan's vocabulary. Sometimes he just seemed to love being part of a family, and we toyed more than once with the idea of bringing him back to the UK at the end of the tour. If we didn't it could almost be guaranteed that he would be conscripted into the army, to be yet another fatality.

But it was to Vietnam he wanted to go. Heaven alone knows to what indoctrination he had been subjected for him to be so convinced of the glamour of war. At any rate, it wasn't yet, but as the disappearance of money continued, we even became suspicious of him.

"It has to be Pan," Bob said angrily one morning, "You say the girls don't come in after cleaning."

"It isn't. We love Pan. He wouldn't." The two boys defended him stoutly.

"We'll never get to the bottom of it," he sighed. He has that same inscrutable smile they all have when you challenge them. He knows what his sister earns - why shouldn't he feel equally justified in emptying western pockets?"

Thankfully, before we were driven to question his honesty, we discovered our thief. It was Minty, and she was being expertly trained! She loved greatly to give away her works of art to all and sundry, and on Pan's birthday she had painted a special picture.

"Perhaps you should paint one for Chintana and Suan too?"

"No they like *little* pictures," she said simply.

"Well make them a little one," Jon laughed at his sister.

"I can't draw the man."

"What man?" We were intrigued.

"I go and get one." And she scampered off upstairs, returning apparently empty-handed, and yet saying, "I go and give Suan."

The 'little' picture proved to be a 50 baht note, bearing the head of King Bumiphon, neatly folded between the sole of her foot and her flip-flop. The humid conditions ensured that it didn't slip out! And between each toe was a small coin.

"Minty, you never take money that isn't yours." We were simultaneously cross and relieved.

"Not proper money," she said. "See Daddy, no Queen." Though mistakenly and misguidedly, she had applied logic and observation.

What else would she do to surprise us? But oh how easily she had been manipulated. We could only imagine the coaxing and praising that had taken place whenever she had visited Suan and the girls in their huts. Those four simple, unadorned huts that served as homes contained little else than a mat and pillow, whilst outside each door was a klong jar for bathing. In our first week we had been so embarrassed by the contrast of our luxurious conditions and the starkness of those the servants endured, that we bought four mattresses, cane chairs and cushions. Before daybreak the next morning they had all disappeared - sold, we presumed from the amount of candy they ate that day. Possessions we discovered, were encumbrances, and impeded a hasty getaway, should circumstances demand. We had very much lost the upper hand, we were informed by more experienced 'Brits'. We'd have a struggle now to get any sort of co-operation.

It was this feeling that he had lost control that made Bob feel so irritated by the situation. He prepared to go outside, and in his hand, despite the stealing, he had a week's wages for Suan.

"This way, I can tell her to go right now," he said, though we both knew that such an attempt to do things the 'right' way, would be seen as ridiculously British. He returned minutes later, looking distinctly uneasy.

"She had her cooking pots strung together before I had had time to say anything – she's even taken all the charcoal from the stove they share. I wouldn't be surprised at repercussions. We shall probably wake up to some damage."

Making doubly sure that all the doors were locked before going to bed, we were relieved to come down next morning to an apparently undisturbed house. We opened the shutters, and called to let Chintana know we were up so that she could lay the breakfast table. But Chintana was no longer there. Pan crawled out of his hut clutching a deep facial wound.

"Suan tell Chintana ghosts come. She go away. Ghost cut me."

"That was no ghost Pan. Come on you soft head - get in the car." Bob revved up the engine and noisily covered the first hundred yards of the drive before slamming on the brakes. Ahead, was a substantial amount of broken glass, doubtless intended to ensure a puncture.

I rushed into the garden shed for a broom, and decided to lock the kitchen door, which being the one that led out to the huts, was the only one we had not yet opened.

"We'll all go," I said. "This is becoming too much like a Bond movie for my constitution."

His entourage to the hospital delighted Pan, despite his cut, obviously achieved by the swift deft action of a sharp blade, and even more by the attention he received.

Language precluded us from knowing much about him, but having watched many Thai women of Pan's social stratum bravely disappear behind a hedge to give birth, we surmised that he had not seen the inside of many hospitals or clinics. Once dealt with, he wore his bandage as a sign of promotion to the upper echelons, and was more than a little reluctant to relinquish it when the wound no longer required to be covered.

Minty insisted on nursing him all day, dosing him with orange juice and telling him 'stories'. What sort of English pronunciation he picked up we could only imagine!

"Well, we have one left out of four, and he's an invalid! You realise if this notion about the house being haunted persists, we'll all have to move," Bob asserted.

"Surely, nothing so drastic," I replied, simultaneously wondering how everything would get done today. In England, the domestic chores were part of most working women's lives, but here in the intense heat and humidity, such an effort could not be sustained. For the same reason, no servant would agree to cope with more than one aspect of domestic life: thus Chintana had been cook and cared for the dining room and kitchen whilst Suan cleaned upstairs, and did the laundry.

The garden was Pan's area of responsibility, though he doubled as houseboy if we had guests, the latter being preferable to working outside in the heat.

"I'll mention it to Nam at the office this morning - he'll know what to do. That's if I ever get there of course."

He didn't really mind taking Pan to the hospital and he had been over-the-moon that his favourite servant wasn't dishonest, but all the same he needed to make a token protest. "I'll phone your M.D. and explain," I offered.

"Tell Nam to get in touch with Jardines - I'll be over there by eleven o'clock." He glanced swiftly at his watch and snapped his briefcase closed. "Oh look, there's a girl going round to the back door. Evidently the bush telegraph's been in action already."

It had. But the girl had, or affected not to have, a word of English, and I could produce only a few Thai pleasantries and when those were exhausted we resorted in desperation to Pan's hut.

"Tell her about the ghost," I urged. It was no use taking on someone who would leave by the end of the week. Strangely no ghost had ever succeeded in getting a servant to leave before Friday pay-day!

"She called Songwan...she O.K...she have house next to temple."

My expression told him that I did not understand, and he continued.

"Live next to temple wall...no ghost can hurt. Better kill ghost - have number two girl. She have friend Suning."

"How on earth do we kill a ghost?" Pan translated my question for her and they dissolved into the now familiar embarrassed Thai giggling, but all their charades failed to make me understand.

Bob's male secretary Nam brought the answer. He smiled broadly as he bowed his head in Thai greeting.

"You won't believe this Helen," Bob couldn't wait to impart the extraordinary information he had gleaned from Nam on the way home. "It seems an army colonel lived here in this house, and had several men murdered out at the back by the huts - and we're definitely haunted!" He enjoyed every single word. "Of course that's why we've got such a luxury compound at half the price old Richard's having to pay."

"Aren't we the lucky ones," I replied with a distinct lack of enthusiasm. And then, as the awful possibility occurred to me, "Did the colonel sleep in our room?"

"Yep - almost sure to have done - probably in our very bed! Anyway, Nam knows exactly what to do."

"So do I - I'll start looking for another house to rent tomorrow."
Bob winked at the boys who were agog with excitement.

"Oh no, let's catch the ghost," they insisted.
Nam smiled at my dilemma. "Mrs Wade - no need to move. All very simple. We can have ceremony here in garden and say goodbye to ghost. I have seen monks today and they agree to come on Friday at four o'clock. In the meantime I bring joss-sticks which must light each evening. Come, I show you."
We all trooped outside where Pan seemed to have recovered rapidly.

"Only headache now I have."
He did not wish to miss the 'fun' and who could blame him? There was precious little in his life to get excited about and at this moment he was enjoying the unexpected interruption to his routine.

Joss-sticks were positioned and lit and the process was to be repeated each evening until Friday when, as agreed, four saffron robed monks arrived. They proceeded to tie a thick white rope all around the house, and then each man lightly supporting it at intervals, they chanted whatever was relevant to the exorcising of a ghost.

The ghost itself did not worry me for I had never felt in the least haunted and dismissed the whole notion as an irritating timewaster. But living in the house of a murderer most certainly did, though I was urged not to take it too seriously. Life in the East was cheap: such happenings were not uncommon.

It was an experience and a half for the children, and for long afterwards, whenever Minty had a problem, she tied a rope around it! It seemed the monks also knew it was Friday pay-day, for the event cost us dearly.

"You were right - we should have moved!" Bob laughed, digging deep into his pocket. "Fun though, wasn't it?"

Number two girl Suning arrived, and we grew as fond of her as Pan. And yet there was something so elusive about her. Quiet and dignified, she remained a very private person. On her days off she completely disappeared. Returning one day a little late, she appeared flustered and tense. On the third finger of her left hand was a gold band.

"Suning. You're married! Oh why didn't you tell us? We must have a celebration."

"No, no please." It was evident that that was the last thing she wanted. "Ring ...my mother's ..she die."

So that was why she was upset.

"Suning, I'm sorry. Do you need some time off - why didn't you say?"

"No. Everything OK now I work." She removed the ring from her finger, and took it, and herself, to her hut. And I was left with the distinct feeling that one lie had led to another, and was saddened to think we were not as close as I had thought, for she obviously wanted to keep her problem to herself. I had, I knew, failed to heed the warning freely given by the other Brits in the office, not to become involved.

"I've lived here for fifteen years now," Richard, Bob's boss, had told us, "and I'm no nearer to understanding them than on the day I arrived. East and West will never meet; we are worlds apart."

But we were all human, with human emotions, I had thought privately, and that must count for something. And stubbornly I went on believing it.

I asked Songwan, who was much older than Suning, to keep an eye on her.

"Suning sad," I told her, and should have known better than to think Songwan didn't already know all about the friend she had brought here. "What's wrong, Songwan?" I asked.

"Suning married - long time. He bad man."

I was astonished. "A long time? But Suning is only seventeen!"

"Suning twenty-six. He prison."

Her gestures indicated it was for grievous bodily harm, so I assumed robbery was also involved. Poor Suning. And she was such a gentle person, always so clean and trim, taking pride in her work.

It was not many weeks afterwards that Jon, returning with Pan after a visit to his grandmother's which included, it seemed, a diversionary trip to the fairground, came into the sitting room and announced, "Daddy, there's a man in Suning's hut. He glared at me. He wasn't very nice."

Bob shot a glance at me, and raised a questioning eyebrow.

"Could it be we've got an escaped prisoner on our hands now," he whispered as he walked towards the kitchen from where the huts were visible.

But Suning pre-empted our question, and came in to prepare supper.

"My brother," she said nervously. "He go home now."

"Suning, we don't mind you having visitors, as long as you are not made unhappy by them." Pan had followed her through the door, thus blocking our view of the disappearing husband.

Sensitivity and intuition had removed the need for further words on this occasion. Why did they feel they had to join ranks against us? Surely Pan had no cause to be suspicious of us. Maybe Richard was right; I would never really get to know them.

Bob had cause next morning to regret his words to Suning, for immediately after breakfast, Songwan disappeared only to return an hour later with husband and two children. She beamed as she introduced them. "My visitors!"

"I didn't know you had a family Songwan," I said weakly.

"And I thought she couldn't understand much English," Bob muttered.

As always when we appeared perplexed, Pan delighted in the importance of being able to explain. "No ghost. Now Songwan no need house by temple. You happy visitors."

"Servants are your department from now on. Come on let's go on the terrace for a drink," Bob said resignedly.

Neil, always a little wary of new circumstances, remained on the outside of the situation for a while, but Jon, grasping the opportunity of a new friend, quickly took a football onto the lawn, whilst Minty and Songwan's little girl took all of thirty seconds to become acquainted. Mysteriously, for no-one could imagine why, we were soon consuming twice as much sugar again!

Suning became a very frightened and unhappy person, and I begged Bob to enlist Nam's help, but he said only, "You know what Richard advised - just stay out of their lives."

In England we would have gone to the police with our suspicions. Here in this strange exotic country, we learned to think twice before doing anything for which there was no 'Company method of procedure'. But Bob did agree to have Nam to supper so that I could ask him what to do. I told Suning there would be an extra person to the evening meal.

"You know Nam, our Thai friend," I said, hoping she would tell him herself of her worries.

But it was Songwan who served the dinner that evening.

"Suning say Goodbye. She love here, she say tell you."

"You mean she has gone already?"

I realised Songwan would say no more in Nam's presence. His visit had achieved the exact opposite of what I had intended.

"I think better we do not ask questions Mrs Wade," he said sagely. "Often it is better that way."

"But Suning may be in danger," I protested. But he did not comment, and talked of business to Bob. The mysterious Eastern veil had been pulled down on the conversation, and I knew better than to proceed. Songwan found us another girl who stayed with us for well over a year, but things were never quite the same again.

Minty's poor sight proved a frightening handicap on more than one occasion, but especially one evening when, at dusk, she bent down to pick up what appeared to her to be a skipping rope. Pan, not generally renowned for his speed of movement, suddenly leapt from the raised patio, and in a lithe, graceful action, encircled her in his long arm, away from the danger. The skipping rope was a coiled snake. Amazingly to me, for he had been born in Thailand, he too was afraid of the snake, and with Minty still in his arms, gesticulated to me to hurl a rock at its head. His fear was contagious, and seeing no rock immediately to hand, panic-stricken, I brought the garden broom heavily down on the reptile.

Blood spat out, and believing the deed to be done, I involuntarily lifted the broom expecting the snake to die there and then, but it had coiled itself around the broom head, and began to slither down the handle towards my arm. I threw the broom to the ground, whilst Pan, after his initial bravery, decided he had done enough, and rushed off to be sick. With strength that left me gaping, Minty levered an enormous stone from the rockery and dropped it squarely on the snake's head.

"All done," she said calmly, and skipped off to comfort Pan.
The snake had bothered her far less than the mosquitoes that she was deliriously happy to leave behind when we returned to England.

After our two-year tour we brought home her first school report on which her teacher had written, 'We feel we are missing out on a wonderful experience in not being able to watch and perhaps help a little in her future.' If only that teacher knew what a boost she had given us.

Before Bob's tour in the Far East was over, Pan went off excitedly to his war. I confess I was hurt that he apparently felt no wrench, for the children were close to tears, and I couldn't bear to think what might happen to him. I had wanted so much for him to come back to England with us, arrogantly assuming that he might just like our cold damp country if only he had some family. But I suppose when life is as ungenerous as it was to both him and Suning, one did not allow oneself to become attached to either people or possessions. When the contract had expired, we returned to our homeland where Bob began the search for another overseas appointment.

Minty has vivid recollections of her life in the Far East, and to this day refers to them. I recall how soon after we came home, I struggled with heavy shopping baskets to avoid a double journey to the shops. Later she became engrossed in trying to tie string separately around the base and handles of two frying pans and then attaching them to each end of a piece of wood. Unable to manipulate the string, she enlisted her brother's help, showing them at each stage what she wanted, though they were as much in the dark as we. Her poor co-ordination precluded adequate demonstration, until suddenly they realised what she had in mind.

A combination of their greater skill, and her delight and enthusiasm, resulted in a Heath Robinson version of the yoke that the Thai girls wore across their shoulders leaving hands free to serve their customers. Thus equipped they travelled from house to house, delivering delicacies on circular panniers. It was in such a style that Minty planned for me to leave the supermarket, balancing the week's groceries and still retaining two free hands!

Living in the tropics, she and the boys were equally at home on land or in the water, but back at her school in Essex she learned to swim with style in the modest indoor pool proudly purchased as a result of fund raising by the P.T.A. and later vandalised by those with nothing better to do with their energy. More than anything else, her prowess in this field increased her confidence beyond recognition, and it was the key to attempting other activities. Though she has never really mastered skates or bicycle, both demanding balance, she can handle a quiet pony. The school provided a serene, comfortable and secure world, and we owe an immense debt to those who cared for her there over the intervening year before we packed our bags again: this time for Europe.

CHAPTER FOURTEEN

On Minty's tenth birthday our family constituted the total passenger list of the tiny Company Cessna, whose pilot Stan Olwen flew us from our Yorkshire base over to Belgium. Happily tolerant of two young boys who wanted to know how everything worked, whilst their sister offered him slice after slice of birthday cake, he must have found us a very different proposition to the groups of businessmen he normally conveyed.

Depositing us at Bierset Airport with a collection of suitcases, toys, and the cake tin, he seemed reluctant to leave us. "Are you sure you won't let me help you get this little lot to wherever you are going?" he offered with characteristic consideration. Bob assured him we'd be fine. There were warm goodbyes; he wished us luck, gave Minty a kiss, and shook hands with the boys, as a result of which their egos spiralled. Minty and Mum were obviously girls whilst they were chaps! As a result, their tiredness disappeared and picking up a suitcase each, they followed Bob to Customs.

Bob had been over to Belgium frequently in the past months, and had rented half a house, not far from the Ardennes, whose owners, and co-occupiers were a sculptor and his artist wife. The house itself was large, plain and hardly prepossessing from the outside, but its setting magnificent. The office, storeroom and the garage accounted for the ground floor, from which we climbed a rustic stairway onto the balcony that in turn gave access to the lounge. From there we had a breathtaking view down a steep incline leading to the woods and river. We were immediately won over to our new country: and the love of it remains with us still. Since the children were unused to French, school at home was the order of the day for a while, and this took place around the kitchen table from ten until two, followed by a nature ramble in the woods, a visit to a gallery in Liege, or just learning to ask for things in the local shops.

Of necessity, I concentrated on the boys, Minty joining in where and when she could, preferring to be monitor, sharpening pencils and crayons, and serving elevenses, or later, our favourite crusty bread and cheese for lunch. That simple repast was the cause of many an excursion: we were spoilt for choice, and though it was tempting to stay with discovered favourites, we adventurously tried a new cheese at least once a week.

The Goutier family at the farm next door made a great fuss of our offspring, so much so that Minty, who had learned how to say 'Deux litres s'il vous plâit', often played truant during lesson time. Certainly we drank a great deal of milk in those days! One magical day for the three of them, she returned with a white rabbit. "Le lapin," she announced proudly.

"Pookie," shrieked the boys in unison.

Lessons were abandoned, and they took no time at all to piece together a hutch from an old orange box - with the help of Monsieur Wybaux who was persuaded to leave his sculpting for a while. Sharing a garden that was not rendered sterile by virtue of its tidiness, was a constant joy to the boys, and having a resident 'grandfather' who openly delighted in their inventiveness, was little short of heaven itself.

Bob, during the past eighteen months in England, had persuaded his new employers to set up a sales and distribution network in Europe. They supplied industrial oils to the steel industry, and he was to be in sole charge of the operation. And the business got off to a good start; for the time being life was little short of idyllic, if idyllic can include being busier than we'd ever been before. As for the children, learning was the most natural thing in the world.

It wasn't long before the local scoutmaster, who taught modem languages at the secondary school, sought us out, and arranged for the boys to join the cub pack. From then on it was only a matter of time before we were persuaded - and this wasn't difficult because we were delighted for them to have the opportunity - to throw them in at the deep end by enrolling them at l'école primaire, from which time they received all their instruction in French. Whilst the written language presented its difficulties, having only recently begun to cope with their own, they soaked up the spoken word like a pair of sponges. And for years after, when we were again domiciled in England, they returned to go off to Scout Camp with their old classmates and the friendships continue to this day.

We were both bemused and angry when some years later, at sixteen, our youngest son wasn't entered for O level French because he didn't (on paper) conjugate accurately! How we English strangle ourselves with bureaucratic requirements! It would appear that the purpose of learning a language was not after all, to communicate, but rather to decline verbs to impress an examiner.

The demands of the business, and associated entertaining increased rapidly and our evenings frequently involved us in sharing meals with visitors from all over the world in addition to local personnel from Belgium's steel mills.

"Why cook so much for visitors?" Minty asked as she and I busied ourselves with preparations.

"To make sure there is plenty of choice for everyone," I explained.

"And we get a day with no cooking to do after the visitors have gone," Neil added. "We can eat all the left-overs, and have extra time for fun."

So we were to be duly embarrassed one evening, when Ben, an American friend and business colleague, phoned at the last moment to ask if he could bring a Portuguese contact and his wife, whom he thought Bob would be interested to meet.

"He could prove very useful," he promised knowingly.

We hurriedly laid two extra places, and the evening went well until, at the coffee stage, Ben jokingly asked why the children were looking somewhat crestfallen. I guess he did it more to include them in the conversation thinking they were bored than because he wanted a reply, but Minty, who did not know how to be either devious or subtle, provided him with one.

"Uncle Ben, you and the man and lady have just eaten our fun day - it's all gone!"

Ben saw the amusing side of the situation and, fortunately, the Portuguese couple hadn't understood Minty's choice of phrase. But certainly her choice of phrase left us in no doubt when, on another occasion, Bob had the distinct impression that there were fewer beers in the fridge than he recalled putting there, but as we had so many visitors, and Monsieur Raway the accountant often stayed over the lunch hour, it was not our habit, or inclination, to notice anything other than the need to restock the fridge.

He casually mentioned it to the boys, but receiving no positive or indicative reaction, he did not pursue the matter, until a few days later he had the same impression.

"Now if somebody isn't telling me the truth..." Bob began, but both sons protested their innocence.

"One of them is being mighty cool about it...I wonder if making shandy was something they learned at cub camp?" He was more concerned about the lie than the missing lager. He questioned them again indeed several times and was exasperated by their apparent complicity in evading the truth. But silently admitting defeat he let the matter drop.

Once a week I cleaned each of their rooms and as I emptied Minty's waste basket into a dustbin liner, I heard the sound of empty tins, never for one moment connecting the sound with the missing lager, but wondering if she had disregarded a 'treasure' by mistake, I investigated. We had found the culprit! She hung her head in shame when faced with the situation, much to the amusement of the boys who were obviously enjoying the proof of our misplaced suspicion.

"Minty, you know it was very wrong to take something without asking. Why did you do it?"

She looked at her brothers, not just for moral support, but for an indication of what to do next. This was a novel situation indeed - the boys actually witnessing *Minty* in trouble!

Bob repeated the question slowly. "Why Minty?"

She certainly couldn't invent, or think on her feet. We knew that her answer, when she did find words, would have to be the truth. Quite suddenly, and surprisingly decisively, she looked us straight in the eye, and used one of Bob's own phrases to supply us with the answer we seemed to her, to require.

"Boy, did I need a beer!"

Intending to be cross when the confession was finally made, it was all we could do to stifle our laughter. Indeed the boys made no attempt, and fell about in hysterics. And their sister, previously contrite, now responded to their adulation with sheer delight.

"I've been naughty too!" she cried triumphantly-

When we eventually managed to keep our faces straight, we told her that she would have no pocket money for a week. But we knew that the success of emulating the boys would have been worth a year's deprivation. What price being one of the crowd!

Single-handed Bob took on American competition and succeeded in gaining orders that ensured the upward spiralling of the business. So confident was he that he had put his job on the line when persuading his boss to allow him to set up a Central European Office, and I was glad that no humble pie was on the menu.

His energy in making contact, to which he held tenaciously, was seemingly inexhaustible. Days chasing contracts, and then often hours in the steel mill making observations through the nightshift: I found it fascinating to watch how the adrenalin of success dispelled fatigue. He loathed the associated office work, but was reluctant to add a secretary to the payroll. "We can go on managing that side of things between us," he claimed. "Besides, I'd rather take on a rep. That way we can make more business, not paper mountains."

With the boys now doing well in the local school that we had initially agreed to adopt as an experiment some seven months previously, I could find no argument to his suggestion. Having taught them at home until July, they had begun the new term in September, and were now switching from one language to the other with enviable ease.

In those early months whilst Bob was setting up the business, the secretarial side had been uncomplicated, but it was now a full-time job. I suspected the real reason he wanted me to continue was that being away from home so much, he generally made contact in the evenings by telex from his hotel, and as I had grown to know many of the mill managers personally too, they would often phone in from the night shift. He wanted to keep it that way rather than have someone shut up shop at 5.00 p.m.

"Just one thing" - I learned to seize my moments in between his rushing from one appointment to another – "if I'm to continue working in the office with an expanding business, Minty and I can't go on spending hours on buses. We've been waiting now for ten months for the mini - I think our loyalty to the U.K. has been stretched far enough."

"O.K. one Citroen coming up. I'll drop by the showroom in the morning."

We had ordered a mini traveller soon after arriving in Belgium.

"I could sell hundreds if only I could get them," the rep had complained. "I've received one for the Motor Show in Brussels, and one to sell! One! Just look at this." And he showed us an unbelievably long waiting list.

A week later, and for the princely sum of five hundred pounds, a Citroen was delivered, undersealed and road taxed. It sounded incredibly noisy, as if it were about to break down from day one, but fifteen years later I sold our Busy Lizzie as she was affectionately known, very reluctantly for two hundred.

Though she was totally happy being our Office Lady, we were aware that things were not ideal for Minty, but were philosophical enough to accept that the world was not going to be perfect for each one of us, all at the same time. At this period in our lives, it was the turn of Bob and the boys to capitalise on circumstances, and we were delighted at how fast both Neil and Jon were becoming bilingual, and what Minty wasn't learning at her school, she was certainly learning in practical skills.

She kept the office tidy, sorted envelopes into sizes and put stamps on the letters at the end of each day, before walking with me down the lane to post them. It gave her immense satisfaction to hand tea and biscuits to visitors; to hang up their coats and make them feel welcome.

Monsieur and Madame Wybaux did not disguise their pleasure when she visited them, for unlike most normal children, she spent long periods, perfectly still and quiet, watching them paint and plan. She didn't sit or kneel, but squatted as she had done with the women in Thailand. Her reward was a small lump of clay that she modelled and remodelled, enjoying its malleability and texture. When it had dried out, 'Grandpère' would fire it for her to decorate. Such pride as she brought in the result of her labours!

Often they called in to remark on the fine weather, and 'might they take her to the park?' A hurriedly filled bag of crumbs for the ducks and off she would go. They had reached a very satisfying stage in their lives when, success achieved, they had time to stand and stare... And they were determined to enjoy every moment of it.

Whenever they prepared for an exhibition, we made sure that she postponed her visits, for they were true artists and demanded perfection of themselves, no matter the cost. Monsieur was always organised well ahead while Madame, only hours before the showing, would suddenly decide to alter a picture. Sparks would fly, and exasperation prevailed until all was packed into the van for the drive to Brussels.

Exhibition time for them meant also exhibition time for Minty and whilst they made their journey, she filled our sitting room with pictures, and because she thought it was part of the accepted pattern of exhibiting, would, prior to our 'entry', remove a painting, and change the colour of the sky or the shape of a tree!

The days were full and varied, and though the workload was formidable, we combined it over the four years with family excursions to Holland, Germany, Austria and Switzerland, driving through the night when the autobahns were quietest. If flights were involved, then Bob always went alone and thrived on the stimulation of being constantly on the move. Germany one week; Greece and Turkey the next.

The place I most dreaded him visiting was Yugoslavia - a country he loved, but one that I had the utmost difficulty in getting telex messages to and from. Tired and frustrated, I would sit in the office until eleven at night desperately trying to make contact, and receiving nothing from the hotel but assurances that he did not exist: they had no such person staying there. This apparent lack of observation did not, however, prevent them from invoicing him for a room!

Combining business with pleasure proved to be the only way we could get a holiday that could actually be planned at more than twenty-four hours notice. All too often, suitcases packed, and everyone raring to go, Bob would say it was impossible - he must see this or that mill manager....get in before the competition... "they are having problems...it's our opportunity to get a foothold." He would assure us that it would only mean postponing our departure for a day or so, but inevitably the reason for which the holiday was delayed led to correspondence to the U.K. or a trip to the manufacturing unit in France. Each day the children would look expectantly into the office to see whether I was at the 'clearing up' stage. Just as we had used all the clean clothes we had packed, and the boys had committed themselves to being able to play in a football match after all, Bob would announce that it was fine to shoot off for a short break.

This less than ideal situation had its obvious domestic consequences, but on the basis of what could not be altered, must be endured, we charted his meetings and visits and planned the occasional holiday with them as an integral part. Fortunately, continental school holidays gave us rather more scope than English ones would have done. The boys attended school on Saturday mornings, and for longer hours during the weekdays than they had previously done at home; and thus the vacations were much longer. We eventually found the key to successful holidays that for us were something to be eagerly anticipated, but which for Bob could not compete with the life he was living as a job. At least this way we could get away within twenty-four hours of the date he initially indicated, which was an achievement indeed, and for him, the high spot would be the challenge of some new business.

Thus it was that the boys learned to ski in Austria - sufficiently competently to leave the nursery slopes very quickly. Jon, like his father, had no fear of the unknown; what others could do, must be possible for him, and with a delighted cry of anticipation he took off at speed. Neil, always the more tentative, observed an instructor who was teaching some yards away, before following his brother down the slope. Both were natural athletes, and from that first 'run' could barely afford the time to stop and eat. Minty and I were happy just to stay upright: the fact that we never achieved any speed was immaterial. She had the same boots, skis, and bobble hat, and thus equipped, she was one of the 'team'.

One summer, during a particularly beautiful week in Switzerland, Bob decided to take the boys on their first climb. We accompanied them for as long as the incline was barely more than a hill. Minty's balance was never good and so we had decided that whilst the mountaineers scaled the heights duly equipped with ropes and rucksacks, she and I would return to enjoy the woods, and eventually we'd all meet back at the car to collect a picnic.

Even here on the wide pathway, she was unsteady and it took some time to retrace our steps. She disliked intensely the unevenness of the ground, and the loose stones, and it was impossible to proceed at more than a snails pace. At this rate I guessed the climbers would be up the mountain and down again, and back to the car before us. So intent were we on avoiding the discomfort of slipping and twisting ankles that we did not notice the change in the weather until a loose rock hurtled down the mountainside. We looked back to see other climbers who were at the point Minty and I had parted company from Bob and the boys, changing their minds about continuing. Further up, the mountain was visible only at intervals through a thick swirling mist. They would already be much higher up - possibly not being able to see either the way ahead or a means of descent.

The car wasn't far now, but we need to hurry to get back to a telephone, and if necessary to raise an alarm. It was only a small mountain; I didn't even know its name, but the boys were young and on their first climb, and they certainly weren't equipped to spend the night on the slopes. Without warning, the rain suddenly came down in torrents. Hurrying is the thing that without doubt Minty is worst at, and that last quarter of a mile back to the car seemed an eternity. But, of course, if we took the car, then Bob and the boys, even if they could get down, would not only have an uncomfortable descent, but a four mile walk back to the village. We must leave the car where it was - Bob had his key with him. Quickly scribbling a note, I left it on the dashboard, and begged a lift with a family who were just pulling out of the space ahead. They spoke a local Swiss dialect and it took some time to explain the situation.

Back at the apartment I switched on the immersion heater and contemplated my next move. I was, I knew, beginning to panic; something Bob would not be doing, whatever the circumstances. By now they would all be drenched and cold. That mist must have evolved so rapidly, wrapping itself around the mountain and obscuring all but its base from view. I would wait for one hour. Perhaps it would clear just as quickly. At six o'clock I must get help.

At exactly two minutes to six, we heard the car on the gravel drive. I rushed to the door, and three bedraggled shivering bodies fell inside, but miserable? Not a bit of it. Sheer elation abounded as they pulled off their boots, thick socks and anoraks and all three stood in the steaming hot bath together, Minty throwing thick towels around their shoulders. Bob grinned (with more than a little relief I fancied) as the boys vied to tell of the adventure.

The mist had enveloped them in minutes, and looking down they had realised that not only could they see nothing, but certainly could not be seen. They had groped for a stream they had crossed not long before, and uncomfortable though it was, decided to follow the groove it made. By the time visibility returned, they were so wet, there seemed little point in struggling on foot, so had sat on their bottoms and finished off the descent in the fastest way they knew.

"Wasn't that dangerous?" I exclaimed handing them each a mug of hot tea.

"Cor, you bet it was Mum. We're lucky to be alive aren't we Dad?" Jon took an eager gulp at his drink.

Bob put on a serious face, and nodded in agreement, and then whispered cheekily as I passed him another towel, "It wasn't exactly the north face of the Eiger, you know! Thanks for getting the hot bath ready." Without this they might have had less enthusiasm - even in retrospect!

"I wonder if it will be in the newspapers?" Neil said reflectively.

Next day, after watching Gruyere cheese being made at a local farmhouse, we agreed to find a mountain for Minty to climb and the boys searched for a suitable mound. She had come in to breakfast wearing a rope and boots, and the boys had joined in the fun by making her a flag, which, 'mountain' conquered, would be ceremoniously stuck into the ground and the hillock named 'Minty's Mountain'.

Today we decided, would lack any kind of drama. I had repacked much of yesterday's picnic, and afterwards Bob and I relaxed in the sun, surrounded by edelweiss, whilst our offspring built a dam with pebbles in a clear shallow stream.

"Oh Bob, thank goodness you have stopped rushing around for a bit. Isn't this just heaven?" We basked in the sheer serenity of our surroundings for just long enough for him to agree he needed a break, when Neil appeared to tell us that Minty was wet through.

"Did she fall in – it's only a few inches deep!"

"No, she used the cake box to pour water on her head."

"What!"

"She says she's ready to go home for *her* hot bath now!"

"I think a business appointment might be less harassing," Bob laughed. "At least I'd have time for my lunch to settle!"

The week passed all too quickly, and we were soon embarking on the return journey which would consume a further three days if the scheduled visits to customers were as successful as Bob anticipated. Without realising it, we were growing used to having a husband and father with whom we more often communicated over a telex machine than in person. Hearing the noise of an incoming message in the evening, the boys would compete to get downstairs to the basement office first, to say 'Goodnight to him, expertly typing in their greeting, followed by 'over and out'.

We had thought that the addition of a representative to the team would enable us to see more of Bob. To Monsieur Munaut, he had assigned the local contracts that he had made certain of, and which merely required servicing, whilst he personally advanced into Scandinavia.

"It's the best way for him to learn the business," Bob maintained. "He's got oodles of bounce and enthusiasm and as soon as he gets to grips with the groundwork, we can share the new markets."

Unfortunately, Monsieur Munaut's bounce and enthusiasm extended also to his driving, and it wasn't long before he had written off his first company car and suffered a broken leg, resulting in absence that curtailed any hopes of new local business. Having the continental attitude to road accidents insofar as they seemed to be a part of everyday life from what we saw on our journey to school each day, he described in lurid detail, his experience of having no alternative than to drive the car through a shop window. "Oh Madame, c'était vraiment un bon!"

The boys were spellbound. And the story only served to increase their idol worship of this effervescent character who had so recently become part of our lives.

As I sat with them in their bedroom that evening enjoying our ritual hot chocolate, Neil said, "I told you Monsieur Munaut was a racing driver. We went round the corner on two wheels once!" I now knew he was referring to the speed our new friend travelled on ordinary roads, and not to a tall story he had told them about a fictitious career on the race track, when they had accompanied him to town one day.

"I think you'll have to put up with my driving from now on," I said, and it did not escape me that Jon gave Neil a nudge as if to say 'I said you shouldn't have told her'.

There had to be some rapid reorganisation and over the telephone, Bob, who was understandably none too thrilled with developments, decided that Munaut should help out in the office, and that should visits to any of the mills be urgently required before he could return, I should be chauffeur. I felt for both of them; the younger man had begun so well, picking up the technical side of the business quickly, and Bob, who surely could not keep up this pace for much longer, desperately needed an assistant.

"Madame," Munaut put down his pen resignedly as we were preparing invoices one morning, and I knew that like Bob, he was frustrated by the confines of the office. "Madame, may I ask you please to drive me fifty kilometres? There is a mill I know Monsieur has not visited yet. I am sure if I could get in there, I could arrange a trial. That would please Monsieur much more than these papers."
Being in the office he had discovered at first hand how vulnerable we were to the consequences of his being out of the field.

I contemplated his suggestion, and wasn't at all sure how Bob would feel. That was not quite true. I knew exactly how he would feel if Munaut went in without the requisite information, and made a mess of it. I stalled. There would be no-one at the end of the phone.. no-one to collect the children, if we were later back than he thought.

"I am sure Annette would help," he said.

His wife was a delightful young woman of whom we were to grow very fond, and yes, of course, she would come. She seemed only too pleased to try and offset any problems her husband's accident had caused.

The venture onto new ground required not one, but three separate visits before Munaut's enormous smile as he rejoined me in the car on the third occasion, told of his success. They both stayed at the house that evening until Bob arrived back from Portugal, Munaut being unable to wait until the next day to recount developments. I think he was a little disappointed at the reaction, but I guessed that on the way back, Bob had toyed with the idea of reminding Munaut that he had taken him on, on a six months trial basis and depending on the result of the insurance enquiry into the accident, he may not be able to make him permanent. Munaut's success today had increased the dilemma.

But something else was not quite the same, and because the change seemed coincidental with the additional team members, I linked Bob's changing attitude over the ensuing months with their arrival. He was fighting as hard for business, and the orders seemed forthcoming, but the fun was disappearing. We entertained a great deal; Bob, if anything more earnestly than before. And yet, perhaps it was just that the earnestness was apparent instead of being concealed by his relaxed, affable manner.

"We have always looked upon him as a character," one mill manager remarked one evening after dinner, as if almost to remind himself, than to tell me.

I didn't concern myself with current affairs to anything like the extent that Bob did or perhaps I might have realized. Though more determined than ever, he became tense, and the hard work that had been meat and drink to him, now began to take its toll. The reason for his tension gradually became obvious. The decline of the steel industry, once begun, rapidly gained momentum and hit us with the force of an avalanche. Less demand for steel meant less demand for

Bob's products, and when the Company decided to fold the European operation it was with immense sadness, and not a little apprehension that we left our 'Sound of Music' home, and returned to England.

CHAPTER FIFTEEN

The depression that ensued for Bob was a battle he would not allow us to help him fight. And because he was such a strong personality, his withdrawal into his own world deprived the family of its usual bubble and good humour. Almost as if he had been away from us in the time we lived in Europe which in the main he had, he appeared to notice things now that he previously had been too involved in the Company, to see before: strangely it was the basic things, like the passing of the years, that had a great impact on him. I became the butt of his bitterness but in fairness he never allowed his frustration to affect his relationship with Minty.

"Why do you look so tired and drawn?" he suddenly remonstrated with me one day.

Only with hindsight years later did I understand that a man can accept the fading of his wife's bloom of youth much more easily, if simultaneously his daughter emerges as a young woman. Though his love for Minty was beyond question, he yearned for a pretty daughter, and said so. Whereas she had been trim and nicely proportioned prior to puberty, now she was heavy, and amply hipped, and no amount of attention to diet seemed to change matters.

She gained nothing in height, remaining at 4' 10". Though ever warm and cuddly, her weight distressed her. She had no interest in anything that would provide exercise, mainly due to her limited sight, no growth potential and very slow mental and physical reaction, it was an unimaginably difficult task to avoid obesity. With

163

characteristic honesty and frankness, Bob helped her to accept what we found impossible to change, and hugged his 'Tessie O'Shea'.

In the months that followed our return home, descriptive job advertisements were pale and insignificant beside the dashed hopes of the job he had loved most. He 'found' himself again by building a house, or rather enlarging and converting the home we had rented out while abroad. Though he hardly realized it at the time, he was building something that would take the place of his Company; something that no-one could take away from him. The physical building replaced the intellectual and mental stimulation of his enterprise in Belgium.

And whereas a lesser person may have been beaten by the setbacks, so again he gained sustenance from them, quickly losing interest in the straightforward and humdrum tasks, whilst the new challenges fired his imagination, and at such time as they occurred, he became his old self again. The boys could not wait to get home from school to throw off their uniform and join in the activity of the day: carrying bricks, mixing cement or helping to drag tarpaulins over unfinished sections.

Minty was less enthusiastic, preferring order and routine, and as her bus dropped her at the garden gate, she would look apprehensively at a newly delivered pile of bricks or the dismantling of something familiar. I reflected that it was the first time there had been a divergence of interests within our young family, and though we pulled together to keep the project going, there were increasing signs of tension.

For over a year, tired by the day's teaching, trying to cook in a never-ending mess of brick dust and alterations; endeavouring at all costs to keep one room at any given time, homely and comfortable, caused the inevitable strain that I could not prevent communicating to Bob.

"For Heaven's sake, can't we get a proper bricklayer instead of you taking ages like this? Then at least you could look for a job." That was cruel; he wasn't mentally ready, and the satisfaction of seeing a dream, albeit a replacement one, grow however slowly, by virtue of his own effort and ability, provided the daily healing of a hurt, the depth of which I was too insensitive to understand. A steady job with regular salary appeared to my conditioned way of thinking, the only answer.

"You've no understanding and even less imagination. Follow the crowd! Conform!"

His angry outburst triggered off a bitter argument that he, with his stronger personality and total belief in, and commitment to, the project he had embarked on, was able to throw off, whereas I allowed it to encroach on my reserves. Ironically, whilst the house foundations were doubly strengthened, those that bound the family unit were under strain.

Even so I could not but admire the single-minded way he applied himself to the enjoyment of what life offered him each day. It took courage to make the most of being unemployed, to concentrate the mind on what *could* be done, and what he would possibly never have the opportunity to do again, once back in a demanding job. So, instead of worrying about the future, or what might have been, by day he built, and in the evenings he added Russian to his languages. Both of these occupations were fascinating to him and completely absorbed him. Filling in application forms much less so, especially when weeks passed without so much as an acknowledgement of them.

"A job will come from contacts, not from these blasted things," he complained.

He went up to London three times each week to follow his language course. What to me would have been a punishing programme of commuting and studying after a day of building, for him replaced the motivation and impetus of his travels in Europe. Contact with people of all nationalities fired him again, and many fascinating characters came out to the house for evenings and weekends. They stepped over piles of bricks and half finished rooms as if it were the most natural thing in the world. Only their intellects were of real importance. They did not in the least find it strange that a man who managed a Company was now building his own house. They too were open to all that life offered; each new circumstance was an opportunity and challenge rather than something to be endured or coped with; factors that only increased my own sense of inadequacy.

As far as a future career was concerned he recognised that he would be competing in a job market with younger men, and saw the mastery of Russian as something that might give him the edge over them at interviews. More firms were now seeking opportunities for trade behind the Iron Curtain and here he thought was his greatest chance.

He lived life as he played bridge; carefully assessing what cards had been dealt to him, and the opposition, then pulling out all the stops. Many times I watched his bridge partner breathe deeply, as Bob coolly lurched them into a slam situation, and bluff the opposition into withdrawing.

And as he always believed it would, the right job did come along. He had used the time prior to it to advantage, whilst I had wasted it on anxiety. He had the courage to stop the world and get off for a while; to take a fresh look at his objectives, and to gain a new sense of direction. But our two personalities seemed less in accord. I longed now for *my* world to stop, and blamed it for not doing so. It never occurred to me that I was the one who was spinning: I the one who must put on the brakes. It takes a special kind of courage to guide our own destinies instead of being jostled along by circumstances.

Whatever our individual reactions, the past two years had been a long period of debilitating uncertainty. The part-time teaching position offered on our return from Belgium, served to cover the day-to-day living expenses, but did not stem the outward flow of our reserves. Original building estimates were to prove optimistically modest but at least the more tangible bricks and mortar offset the fast diminishing bank balance.

Quite unexpectedly the Head asked me to take on full-time responsibility for a class, or else he would re-advertise. My smiled agreement concealed the panic within. Children demand a great deal of time, whether your own or other people's, and as I tackled a pile of mending one evening, I was forced to recognize the overall effect of endeavouring to give all that was professionally and domestically required - and the inevitable extra mile; typing endless applications for Bob in the evenings; becoming involved as part of a family in the house conversion at weekends; and most importantly caring for three children, two of whom had now entered their teens. I was drained, and if honest, resentful of the fact that whilst loving all three children to distraction and wanting to respond to their every need, I had not had time to enjoy them. I wanted so desperately to be fun for them, yet all too often so close to weary tears that living became a tight, routinely controlled, performance.

Minty, who had been almost thirteen on our return to England, had physically become a young lady - a development which, because she looked and felt much as a seven-year old, took both of us completely by surprise. She was bewildered, but only initially frightened. Once she knew it was a condition of becoming 'grown up', it was all I could do to prevent her from announcing it to everybody. I'm certain the milkman did not expect such information when he called! Proud she may have been, but she was pale and drawn as a result, and even after a long time, managing the situation was still beyond her. Whereas previously she had emulated the boys, wanting to do things independently, now she tended to cling to me ever more tightly.

Again, I had attributed less credence to the guilt factor than perhaps I should. Whilst there could not as yet be proof of whose 'fault' it was, and though the subject had not been aired for some years, I knew Bob would never share my sentiment that it did not matter; that a child was born of a couple, not two individuals. So when the news arrived that a Downs baby had been born to his older brother and sister-in-law, his depression reached a new low.

"It was on my side after all," he repeated, stubbornly refusing to be consoled or convinced that Clare being near to middle age, and considerably older than I when Minty was born, there may in fact be no connection. Some years later, Guy's Hospital was to affirm that indeed there was not.

For my part I could only think that at last there would be someone to talk with; not a distant professional but someone close enough to be able finally to open up the wounds and admit their effect; someone bonded by family who would understand as no-one else, having felt and feared and remonstrated with the same emotions. I was very fond of my sister in law, and though I knew it was too early for her to have come to terms with the situation, for me the news was selfishly not depressing, but the assurance I had craved - that I was no longer alone. And in that moment I acknowledged that I too had carried an enormous burden of guilt.

CHAPTER SIXTEEN

Seemingly impotent to relieve him of his angry misery, I feared that Bob was hardly in the right frame of mind to embark on the new job. In the event however, it proved to be the factor that released him from the anguish of the news of his nephew, and he responded with a surprising degree of the old enthusiasm and determination to this latest challenge. He was disappointed to be based in the U.K. and enjoyed nothing like the amount of travel he had clocked up whilst domiciled in Belgium, but nevertheless he saw a fair amount of the world's airports.

Released now of the energy sapping fear that unemployment would be eternal, I determined to do even more with our offspring. But the boys were fast heading towards manhood; less attracted to the ideas I had to offer.

"What say I drive us all to the swimming pool?" I suggested one day.

"We can go there with our friends," was the distinctly unenthusiastic reply.

Ironically, the project I believed had stolen too much time from them, increasingly caught the imagination of Neil and Jonathan, and they astonished me with their practical skills –skills that often proved strong competition to the business of settling down to homework! When Bob returned from business trips, it was often difficult to explain the imprint of their personalities on things he had left unfinished!

Secretly hurt and angry with myself that in this passage through their puberty, I was somehow missing the boat, I could only adore and encourage them as they tested their antlers and made me acutely aware that all too soon I would have to let them go. And as my mind endeavoured to accept that particular fact, so it also grappled with the realization that the little girl whose body having grown impatient of a brain that refused to develop in tandem and was now perplexingly that of a young woman's, would need us more and more. Confused and upset by the pendulum movement of her emotions, she constantly sought assurance that 'sad feelings wouldn't keep coming to bother me'.

I suppose that in normal circumstances, we would have sat quietly together to talk about what was happening and to discuss her future potential for motherhood. Except that for Minty, the fulfilment of babies, whilst cruelly possible, must be denied her. I observed how increasingly she focussed her attention on her brothers, and wondered often what was going on in her mind. They had long ceased to be playmates, and towering above her in height, they needed only to put an arm affectionately around her shoulder and whisper they hadn't had time to make their beds or tidy their rooms, than she would scuttle off delightedly to rectify matters, for her greatest joy now came from being needed by them; they, who could do so many things to which she couldn't begin to aspire. If with all their apparent skill they still sought her help, it suggested they hadn't overtaken her to the point where she had actually lost them.

I reflected on how tremendously the gap had widened. In Bangkok she had gone to school with children only two years her junior. Now each year saw a significantly greater differential between her ability and that of her younger brothers. She was indeed the hour hand on the clock that Neil had once described in those far off days when we were frequent visitors to the local hospital, and when, within the tight little family unit, her slowness mattered not a jot. And now? Was that why they hadn't wanted to go to the pool?

170

What scurrilous comments had they encountered in the outside world; what vindictive ribbing suffered on the school bus? At some cost to themselves, I suspected, they insisted the subject had never arisen. It was a protective stance they maintained for many years; indeed, until they reached an age and maturity when such comments were worthy only of derision, and could not dent their affection for her one iota. She was their sister who had welcomed them into the world: they would see that the world did not harm her.

Nevertheless, she was aware of a changed attitude from the public whenever she and I went shopping. There were fewer amused, compassionate glances than in the days when she was a little scamp who was obviously handicapped. She moved more slowly now, her gaze less focused and yet she was uncomfortably conscious of the stares of strangers; stares that were furtive and prolonged. Disturbed to be the subject of curiosity, her hand sought mine more often, until eventually she did not bother to withdraw it.

It soon became evident that she was looking at her brothers as role models for future boyfriends. And therein lay the contradiction of human nature. The boys surpassed her in terms of ability and expertise - by comparison she was a mere child, yet ahead of them, despite her handicap, she was aware of the social dictate that she should have a mate. To be frank I feared the consequences of such desire, and yet, when I questioned her, it was to discover that the longing was not yet a physical urge which might propel us into catastrophe, but to wear a beautiful flowing gown, to ride in a chauffeur driven limousine; in essence to be an utterly feminine centre of attention. I picked up on the fantasy element and asked who Prince charming was to be.

"Oh, you find someone for me," was the response!

"And where will you live Minty?" Jon joined in the make believe.

"I live here. All the time I live here," she stated unequivocally, firmly consigning the other half of the partnership to a somewhat hazy future.

In between our overseas tours, Minty had attended the same special school at which she was first enrolled at five. Now ten years later she, and those of similar age, were being prepared by staff, for the next stage of life. It was a difficult time for parents for whom there were really only three options to be considered. The Adult Day Training Centre could take only a certain number, which in uncomplicated terms meant that they could reject the most severely handicapped on the very true basis that they did not have the staff ratio to cope. The already unfortunate parents of these children were faced with the choice of placing their son or daughter in care at a residential centre forty miles away, again if there were places available, or looking after them at home.

Having visited the Adult Centre on one morning a week for over a year, Minty at seventeen, was anxious to take the next step. She was becoming more interested in the opposite sex as 'heroes' and 'idols', and the means of achieving a fantasy world depicted in the American soaps. Expecting a similar set-up to her present surroundings, I made an appointment to view one day in the school holidays, and could not have been less prepared for the shock.

"It's dreadful," I told Bob when he got home that night. "Dismal and dreary—obviously hasn't had a coat of paint since the year dot. The manager told me that they are always at the end of the queue where finance is concerned...the last to get any grants."

"What does Minty think of it?"

"She can't wait to go. She only notices the people inside."

"Doesn't that rather decide matters?"

Whereas previously we would have discussed the issue at length, this, as most topics now, was curtailed precipitately and in any case, I had to concede - simply because I couldn't come up with an alternative.

Bob had more than a few problems on his plate these days, mainly in the form of manufacturing difficulties, and my objecting to something Minty was obviously keen on was a complication he could do without. At least that was the reason I gave myself for the silence that followed, for I didn't want to admit that there could be a more fundamental reason.

And so off she went, oblivious to the peeling paintwork and grimy walls. The uncarpeted floors were not a disadvantage, for did they not facilitate dancing to records in the lunch hour? She had entered an adult world; a world that afforded more freedom, and yet which, by virtue of its less directed lifestyle, forced her into becoming more acutely aware of what she was missing. Talk between the girls was invariably of romance and pop stars and just as in the normal world, so Downs Syndrome people, often short and dumpy, were frequently rejected in favour of those who were slim and pretty, and whose retardation was obvious only when they spoke.

Minty suffered many a heart-break, for she was passed over by the very ones she yearned for - the young men whose appearance most resembled that of her adored, now six foot tall brothers. Though her friendships included many Downs syndrome fellows, none could hold that special attraction for her. The loneliness that resulted, generated the writing of scores of letters to stage and television stars.

I would argue with any who claim that actors and performers are selfish, conceited individuals, for her proudest possession is an album of letters and photographs of those to whom she wrote; not just photographs hastily put into an envelope by paid office staff, but replies bearing kind, individual messages to her. Many recognised the painstaking hours that were involved for her to produce a legible letter - and they responded in their dozens.

Paul Eddington, of 'The Good Life' and 'Yes Prime Minister' fame, revealing immense compassion and understanding, personally wrote two foolscap sides by hand. A large framed photograph of the 'Only Fools and Horses' team sent by David Jason, hangs above her bed. And from Val Doonican, to whom she had sent a special home-made Oscar in clay, because he hadn't won one that particular year, she received an invitation to his dressing room at the Cliffs Pavilion in Westcliff. Her delight knew no bounds when taking her on his knee, he gave her a picture he had painted of a cottage in Ireland. He told her the Oscar was 'much nicer than the Academy Award, and that it had a very special place in his study'. He actually went on stage late, because of the time he spent with her. A most genuine and compassionate man. She still has his painting, prominently displayed, to this day.

And so the TV stars became her best and all important friends. She switched on their programmes as meticulously as she would have kept appointments with them, and never failed to write and 'encourage' them. And her joy was as great as theirs apparently when they appeared on Wogan - the barometer that evidently indicated arrival in the celebrity class!

"Will I ever be on Wogan?" she asked frequently, not because she expected fame to touch her, but because she believed that all who appeared on the show, lived together in the studio at Shepherd's Bush, and a visit would bring her into contact with all of them at one wonderful party! And thus she added magic and fantasy to her life, to replace the social freedom of which she was deprived. Not for her the 'dream come true', but almost certainly the dreaming.

Though the speech that for so long evaded her as an infant, has for many years enabled her to hold conversations, she retains her own inimitable style. There are some words and phrases that are just too amusing to change. 'Isn't he a marble', she will say of someone who has been of practical help to us. And when I went into hospital, she told all and sundry I had gone to have my 'asparagus veins' taken out!

Her birthday is the high spot of the year. Immediately one is over, so we plan the next. When she was young, she delighted in the arrival of aunts and uncles with their children, but of course, they grew up and left home whilst Minty remained with us. When she transferred to the Adult Centre, so the nature of her parties changed. Just once a year she was allowed a 'wing-ding' with up to twenty or so her of colleagues. Her bus guide, driver, group leader, and anyone who was closely connected -and therefore automatically loved by Minty – also came to join in the fun for the evening. Her eighteenth was particularly memorable. Friends had been invited from seven to ten 10pm. The first ones arrived at 3!

"We just couldn't wait," they admitted frankly!

Being a little more independent than most, and living at the residential home they had caught the local bus.

"We aren't allowed to go on the bus after dark," one explained.

"So you are going back with someone else's Mum or Dad?" I asked rhetorically, simultaneously putting another batch of cakes in the oven.

"If we can get a lift," one of them said, unconcernedly, though with absolutely no intention of being discourteous, "but if we don't, we'll stay here with you till morning."

I wondered how many others had exactly the same intention!

"Did you invite Mark and Paul?" I asked Minty "You should have told me, sweetie."

"No I didn't ask them," she added, "but isn't it nice - now the party will be even bigger."

I gave up, quite unable to reduce life to such simple terms. How uncomplicated they all were!

Trying to sound totally unconcerned, I turned to Paul. "Do you think any more of your friends intend to come?"

"They were all phoning for taxis when we left," he replied simply, and was perplexed that both Bob and I stood rooted to the spot. "But they won't get here," he continued in explanation.

"How can you be sure?" Bob asked, still aghast.

"Cos they didn't put any money in the call box. They're not very bright you see. We have to help them a lot!"

In the event there were only a few gate-crashers (though they would have been horrified to be so called), and the party went on with a swing all evening. Time seemed quite meaningless, and 10 o'clock found us all doing a conga around the house, and parents who came to collect their youngsters at the appointed hour, instead of going home, joined in. We finally sang Auld Lang Syne at 1 a.m.! Adults who normally felt uncomfortably conspicuous because they had produced a handicapped son or daughter, were released from their guilt, inhibitions and complexes, and sang their Golden Oldies, and danced Hands, Knees and Bumps-a-Daisy as if they hadn't a care in the world. For those three hours we were relieved of the burden that is born of sharing the exclusion of the handicapped from so great a part of the normal social world: tonight we *were* the world. Tonight there was no need for apology, embarrassment or explanation: tonight we were not *bound* by our love of them, but *freed* by it. And no-one wanted it to end.

And so, each year afterwards, we had a different theme, never quite knowing, because of the difficulties of replies, transport, and general communication going awry, who was going to turn up. A great success was the Gipsy Party - fancy dress, of course - at which a long-standing friend became Gipsy Petulengro, and told fortunes with the aid of his crystal ball. He gained his clues from their general conversation, and not realising this, they were entranced by his accuracy. It would have been all too easy to promise glowing futures of tall dark strangers, but having shared our parties for many years, he was sensitive to the credence they would attach to his 'predictions', and confined his forecasts to 'a pleasant surprise before the end of the day' and the like.

The Country and Western too was a hit, as guitar-strumming cowboys wooed the Texas gals, and then whirled them in the direction of a fried chicken supper. And at a Cabaret Party, the guests provided the entertainment for each other. Being natural mimics, 'turns' were both earnestly performed and hysterically received.

But quite the most successful was the D.I.Y. party for her twenty-second birthday. I had prepared a number of dishes to the point where they were eighty per cent finished. Another guest partnered each of Minty's handicapped friends, and together they completed the preparation in time for all to sit down for a 'feast'. Minty iced and decorated her own birthday cake, whilst friend Eddie chose the trifle. The jelly having set the previous evening, he spent a blissful hour, totally absorbed in the decoration of it - and then promptly covered all his handiwork in lashings of cream! "Now it'll taste good," he announced proudly (this was obviously far more important than just *looking* good!). Lynne prepared a plate of chequered sandwiches, the filling being quite the heftiest part of them, whilst a somewhat chunky salad emanated from the hands of Paul and Tim.

All wore chefs' hats, as they paraded with their gourmet delights, around the house, past a panel of grandparent-judges, before placing them on a central table for the important business of eating them, having first been duly admired and photographed. Of course, the standard was so high that no outright winner could be decided upon, and prizes for all were distributed accordingly!

By tradition now, and just prior to the blowing out of the candles, Bob would make a speech for Minty and then she would be called on to reply. A little flashing of the eyelids, and a coy smile preceded her carefully practised words of thanks to everyone for coming, for their gifts and please would they come again next year. Noisy acceptance and affirmation followed, and another party would proceed to its end.

Sitting down together for what we considered a well-earned drink when everyone had gone home, we wished they could each have one party a year so all have enjoyed a regular social life of their own. But we had to accept that most Downs babies were born to middle aged parents, and many of those of Minty's friends would now be in their seventies for whom the organisation of a party would be too exhausting.

And yet we wondered if stigma still obtained, even for those whose children were themselves handicapped. Impossible and illogical though it may seem to an outsider, it is so easy to be blinded by love to the symptoms of retardation in one's own child, and yet still to be initially repulsed by those same signs in others, no matter how great the understanding.

177

As the years passed, Minty watched with longing, the comings and goings of our sons, and their girl friends, and the independence that rapidly accrued to them. "When can I take a driving test?" she asked wistfully. "When will I have a car?"

We managed to circumvent that one, by explaining that sight is so important to drivers, and because she had had so many operations when she was younger, it might be better if she became our 'navigator' on journeys instead.

But there was no such easy way out when, some years later, her brothers were married. At both weddings, she wore a longed for pretty dress - one peach and one cream, but while she proudly stood behind the bride on the first occasion, she was less excited the second time. This bridesmaid business was all very well, but there was no mistaking she desperately wanted to be the bride on whom all attention focused. She yearned for the smiles, the photographs, the confetti and the well wishers -and now, with physical development having taken place as with any other adult, most of all, for the fella.

And there was no mistaking the hurt. Always in the past there had been at least a part-solution to the problems of being handicapped; something we could do to alleviate the pain. We had attempted to explain that not everyone marries, and that not everyone who did was happy; that for handicapped people it was especially difficult. Though she did not protest, we knew that she was not allowing our words to penetrate; though she heard them, she refused to absorb them for she recognised them for the sham that they were.

Only Bob had the courage to be frank and tell her that she almost certainly would not marry and could she be very brave and share her life with us instead. We were to discover that she had her own solution to the problem. Whilst she told others that she was not going to leave home, but would stay to look after *us,* so there began a fantasy world, created in the privacy of her own room. She taped her favourite programmes and played them over and over again until she knew the dialogue by heart, at which point she would 'move in' as the heroine, responding to the taped voice of her current idol.

She persisted in her optimism in much the same way as she decided to continue to believe in Santa Claus: because it was so much more pleasant than *not* believing. And so we had the contradiction of a young woman who wanted to marry just as everyone else did, and yet who clung to the magic of her childhood. Perhaps it is what we all do, only those of us who have the privilege of independence and marriage, can relive our childhood in the natural progression of children and grandchildren.

We were placed in something of a dilemma to realise as time passed, that despite being intellectually backward, retarded youngsters have the same physical desires as everyone else. Weekly visits with Minty to the Gateway Social Club opened our eyes to the very real need the handicapped have to form relationships, irrespective of whether or not they could be sustained. One Saturday morning we attended the marriage of one of her group - he was not Downs, but certainly retarded - who subsequently lived with his new wife in sheltered housing. Provisions were sometimes made, following a period of assessment at the residential hostel, for friends to share homes, usually in groups of three, with a Warden to oversee the routine daily organisation. It was doubtful that Minty would be considered for such a scheme; indeed we would have been somewhat anxious if she had, for her defective eyesight meant that she could not read the dial on the cooker or iron, but she was nonetheless increasingly drawn to the young men in her group.

It is an enormous responsibility to deprive another of the chance to have children, but we didn't feel it was a decision she could rationally make for herself, and after long deliberation we agreed that she should enter hospital for a hysterectomy. Bob thought this was somewhat drastic, and worried lest she should lose her femininity, but the consultant persuaded him that if she were to be deprived of having children, then the least we should do for her was to deprive her also of the monthly inconvenience.

Inevitably she was admitted to a ward for women who had reached either the age or decision to have no more children. She must have listened to a great many 'female' conversations concerning the 'time of life', but obviously had the greatest difficulty in applying any word associated with men, to the female condition. She had her question ready for us that evening as we entered the ward for visiting hour.

"When will I have my ladypause?"

It was a tough few days for her, for she really didn't understand why she was there, or the need for an operation if there was no pain. Rightly or wrongly we said that the operation was to make sure she wasn't bothered any more with her 'lurgy' with which she had had to cope from the age of twelve. It was just asking too much to have to tell her not only that she wouldn't have her wedding day, but that she would never have a baby either. The night she came home, I bucked against the unfairness of it. There seemed no answer to such a simple question as 'why'?

The size and shape of her bedroom lent itself to conversion into a bed-sit, the next best thing to being married and having a place of her own. For years and years she had spent her gift tokens on picture puzzles and felt tip pens. Now she purposefully accompanied me to department stores to buy an electric kettle, portable television and coffee maker. She 'raided' the kitchen for teacups and trays until her little nest was complete.

And to this little world she so artistically created, she invited us each evening for coffee, though we were firmly given the elbow when one of her favourite programmes was due. Little did she know that these invitations were the sticking plaster that held us all together for a little longer.

Without her downstairs, we lacked the effort and motivation to keep our relationship the solid one it had been for so long. Something was not only missing, but destructive, and neither of us understood. Though we had the proximity of each other, each was lost and lonely and afraid. We knew it had begun when we returned from Belgium. The lustre had gone from our lives. Neil and Jon, instead of having the daily challenge of communicating in a second language, and eventually transferring to the International School in Brussels, attended the local comprehensive. Bob himself had to ask permission or wait for a directive to visit customers, a situation he described as feeling bound and gagged, and which several years later caused him to take the decision to leave the world of commerce and return to teaching. And though they had been infrequent, Minty and I so missed our occasional coffees and gateaux at the pavement cafes in the Place de la Cathédrale in Liege. It wasn't only that we were not doing what we wanted to do, for how many people can? But much more important, we weren't living a full life, and that mattered enormously. And yet it was something we grew to accept, and the passing of time faded our memories, and as with most families, to a greater or lesser degree, we developed a steady, if humdrum rhythm of emotional limbo.

Though at opposite ends of the spectrum in personality, neither of us was one to compromise. Saddened and frustrated that we were drifting into a mere shared existence - something we had despised in others - we searched for the bond that had once been so evident. Something was slipping through our fingers, and we seemed powerless to stop it. Bob was ever the colourful exciting half: I the quiet predictable one, a combination that inevitably had its hiccups. Disagreement and anger there had been in the past, but now the very fibre of our marriage seemed under attack. One small word out of place could send shock waves through the foundations.

Worst of all, the lack of trust in each other's motives for doing the most ordinary things, became apparent. We came home looking forward to being together and yet within minutes, we were resenting each other's presence. Both, over a long period, tried to find the way, but despite our resolution and strenuous effort to change the course of events, the quarrels continued, indeed escalated.

At a strained breakfast one Saturday morning, Minty asked the question she had asked daily for over twenty years. 'Dad, do you love me?' Her total lack of subtlety and inhibition had enabled her to ask each day for the reassurances of our love. Something perhaps we all need, but are too conditioned to do. There must be such security in the voiced affirmation.

And as always, the initial reply, 'Um...I don't know...' It wasn't an effort for him to joke because the interplay with her relieved him from the awkwardness of the silence between us that even so was preferable to the stilted conversation we sometimes managed to achieve.

"Oh Dad, you do. You're only joking aren't you?"

"Course I love you - best in the world."

"Millions and millions?"

"Trillions and trillions."

We were well rehearsed in the follow up. "How much do you love Neil, Jon, Mum..." until she had ascertained that everybody's quota of love was identical, simply so that everyone should be happy and the world ever a lovely place.

But this morning came the bombshell.

"Do you love me more than Mum?"

There was no reply as Bob affected to tussle with a chewy piece of toast.

"Don't you love Mum any more, Dad?" She was obviously not going to let go. I wanted to get up from the table on some pretext, but I knew Minty's intuition was in full flood and one hundred per cent reliable, and tactics would not fool her. He looked at me with expressionless eyes, and then so gently at Minty, to whom I realised at that moment he had never lied.

"I don't know, darling."

"Will you love her tomorrow when you're not cross with her?"

"I don't think so, Minty."

The confession she forced, drained him, and he went out into the garden. The sort of energy that only anger and frustration can produce would go into his digging.

Minty enclosed me in her arms, and with innate empathy she spared me the platitudes whilst simultaneously sharing the rejection. For some time now she had stopped saying 'it will be alright when

Dad feels better', for she knew as well as I that something very deep was troubling him though he would not allow us to be part of it. And so we stayed, with her warm cheek next to mine, and because her arms were too short merely to put one round my shoulder, she continued to envelop me with two.

In the intense sadness, there was no feeling of unwarranted hurt or the smugness of being the injured party, for when I dredged my real feelings - the murky ones we suppress most of the time - I knew that had Minty posed me the question, whilst I may not have had the courage to be so honest, I would have entertained the same doubt, for truly, I did not know, either. But the difference about this morning was that the doubts were no longer a secret. Something had gone sour, not suddenly, but gradually over the years. It was only the realisation that perhaps we were at the end of the road that was shocking in its suddenness.

"Minty, I think Dad could do with a hug; he's very unhappy too." And immediately I questioned whether I had said that because I cared about him or because I needed to be alone. I felt I wouldn't know the real reason for anything ever again. But I did know that a watershed had been reached.

I supposed normally - for wasn't divorce becoming the norm nowadays - the two parties would reach some agreement on how to proceed in separate directions. Only I never felt that Bob was the norm - he was much too strong a character to be dictated to by circumstances. His handling of the house extension after the Company folded had proved that. He had carefully planned it, and from the building of it, had gained his greatest sense of achievement and satisfaction, second only to that which he had experienced in Belgium. Whatever plans we made, there was no way I was going to topple the dream he had turned into a reality. Three Farthings was the family base, and for as long as we both wished it, it would remain so.

And as if to affirm my own feelings, he suddenly appeared at the doorway, grim faced, and clutching his spade as if it were a lance.

"And don't you think you are going to do what the rest of your sex does at times like this," he bellowed. "I built this house and you are not going to ruin it all. And what's more, you can take out that damned almond tree you've planted. It'll stop the sun setting on the veg."

Oh for a sense of humour at that point! But it was never my strong suit.

"Keep your house, and I'll keep my almond tree!" was all I could respond.

The following weeks passed in a stupid and debilitating stalemate situation and I was grateful for every opportunity that occurred for the demand of our separate attention.

One Saturday morning, Bob had gone for a game of squash with a colleague, and Minty was due at the dentist.

"I'm sorry, we're running late," the receptionist apologised. "We've had two emergencies this morning."

Minty had already installed herself in the familiar waiting room, and had picked up a magazine for each of us. Irritated by the prospect of a long wait and frustrating waste of time, I debated whether to pop out to the shopping parade for items I had intended to collect on our way home. Minty made up my mind for me.

"You go and get the shopping: I'll be alright."

I knew she would, because she had seen the same dentist, whenever we were in England, since before she could walk. In fact her affection for him had, in the past years, developed into hero-worship, though he was, of course, oblivious to the effect he had on her.

"She can have a cup of coffee with me," the receptionist offered. "She'll enjoy sitting at the desk."

Despite being open for business until well after midday, there was a something about Saturday mornings that allowed a semi-holiday atmosphere to prevail. Hardly had she said the words, than Minty was beside her.

Leaving the surgery, I walked briskly to where I had parked the car in a lay-by, intending only to collect a shopping bag. A car pulled up beside me, and a man of late fifties wound down the window. He was glancing down at a scrap of paper in his hand. "I'm looking for Jackman's Lane. I can't be far away for it says it's off the main road, but I don't seem able to locate it. Appletree Cottage is the name."

"It isn't far, but I'm not surprised you keep missing it. It's at the back of a small copse, and leads from a turning you should have been given off the main road. Actually it would be quicker for me to lead you there than to explain."

"If you're sure it's no bother..."

We were outside the cottage in less than five minutes. He got out of the car and I saw he had an estate agents key with him. "What a perfect spot. Are you hoping to buy it?"

"No, it's not for sale. The owners are abroad, and I'm looking for somewhere to rent."

I guessed he had come to lecture at the Management Centre not far away.

"Looks as if you've found the ideal place," I remarked. "Must be Elizabethan. Beautiful. No wonder they don't want to sell."

"Have a look inside if you like. That's what I'm here for. Though I don't think it's quite what I'm after. Just look at the garden....must be half an acre." The invitation was irresistible.

"I can't believe Elizabethans were a whole foot shorter than me," my companion remarked as we bent to enter each room. "It's a bit cluttered, isn't it?"

"But beautifully so."

Indeed it appeared as if its owners had merely gone shopping instead of to another continent, for their pictures, china and even silver were still in place awaiting their return.

He laughed. "I've never watched anyone fall in love with a cottage before. 'Fraid it's not for me though. I've got a whole lot of my own stuff to house whilst I look for somewhere to buy. I'd never get it in here. No I'll have to go and look at the others."

"You aren't going to take it?" I asked. I was experiencing one of those rare times in life when one is pushed so unequivocally by providence that the feeling is almost physical. Whatever thoughts and plans I had had at the beginning of this day, I was now standing in the middle of a cottage that was almost demanding I moved in.

"May I......would you let me have the agents name?"

"How strange. You don't mean to say you were looking for somewhere too?"

"I wasn't..."

"But you know someone who is. Yes, of course."

He handed me the crumpled bit of paper, then coughed to interrupt my contemplation of an enormous step. "I'm sorry, I really do have to go now if I'm to find anywhere this weekend."

"Of course. Forgive me."

We drove off in opposite directions; he to look for a more suitable house, and I, not to the shopping parade, but to-the nearest call box. I swallowed hard on hearing the rent, and long before we got home, unmistakable fear was setting in. Why was there a need to change? Why couldn't things be as they had always been? But they weren't and something had to be done to halt the rot before it destroyed us as people. I told Bob about the cottage that evening.

"If that's what you want."

"It's not what I want. But we don't seem to be able to sort things out under the same roof. Everybody's getting hurt like this."

Yet again, we weren't able to discuss matters, and a taciturn silence ensued. I phoned the agent on Monday, and said we would move in the following weekend.

Somehow we all found the courage, or was it cowardice - for there is such a fine line between the two - to go through with it. The car filled with her belongings, and with one almond tree sticking out of the boot, Minty and I turned our backs on the home and the person we loved. Seeing him in the wing mirror, I knew that if he so much as beckoned to us to go back, we would have gone no further. But he remained still until we turned the corner out of his sight.

CHAPTER SEVENTEEN

Putting a key in someone else's front door is a strange and lonely sensation. Minty had been tense on the short journey here, but as she entered the cottage, it had the same effect on her as I had experienced the week previously, only she was able to put those feelings into words more accurately and honestly than I, being uninhibited by fates apparent intervention.

"It's been waiting for us," she said simply. "We can get better here."

It was the first time she had expressed her observation of the strain on us all. We unpacked her possessions and I said that when we next went shopping I'd get her a ceramic nameplate for her door to replace the one that said 'Lindsey's Room'.

"But this is Lindsey's room. I'm just going to look after it for her while we are here. I like the cottage," she said.

So she felt safe here. We had reached first base. All that mattered now was that we should get round the full course without being 'caught out'! For once back at fourth, did the rules not say a further innings was allowed? Even so, I did not underestimate the risk we had taken.

It was idyllic when we commenced our tenancy in the autumn, for the whole month of October was a spectacle of changing colour, both in and beyond the garden, and I took full advantage of the view before leaving for school, gaining both pleasure and sustenance from it. But with no central heating, and a severe winter, our resourcefulness was tested to the ultimate. Each night we cocooned our flimsy Citroen in a sheet of plastic, and in the morning, crossed fingers and toes that it would tick over and start. We put the cold ashes from the wood fire in the sitting room onto the ice, so that once engaged, the car wouldn't slither down the steep drive.

Sometimes it was so cold that we brought the duvets downstairs and slept on the ample sofas by the fire. And Trojan courage was necessitated next morning to brave the bathroom in which the bar of soap had frozen to the sink overnight!

We learned how to use the chainsaw to effect, and cut our logs in the sturdy wood-cradle. There was so much to do just to survive in such an old house that the days passed more quickly than they might otherwise have done. I got up early to light the Rayburn - hoping it would not have gone out by the time we came home, and as soon as we came home, carried in hods of coke to last the evening. We plugged the gaps that allowed such energetic draughts to penetrate and dealt with blocked chimneys, leaking roofs, doors that stuck and windows that blew open. Indeed these minor traumas became so routine that we became acutely conscious of, and very grateful for, days *without* domestic dilemma! We certainly took nothing for granted.

Despite the months apart, the invisible bonds were irritatingly strong. Other people seemed to separate with such businesslike ease, or perhaps it was because they parted to make new links that made it easier, whereas Bob and I had chosen to give each other time and space.

We did not need to communicate that neither was seeing anyone else; the persistent pain was proof of that. It felt as if we were part of a rough tear in tweed cloth: weft and warp, intertwined over twenty-five years, the good bits and the bad - grey threads and gold, and the tear had caused not one, but many threads to break, each one with its own individual hurt. The temptation to go home was strong, but it was evident from the tension when we met, that no healing process had taken place, and so we stuck our ground, each knowing, but not admitting, that we were making no more of a success of our separation than we had made of the last years of our marriage.

Bob too, found himself on a mental see saw. One evening would be spent phoning us, asking repeatedly that we return, another being convinced we had done the right thing - we could be friends with the freedom associated with separation. But neither capitalised on that freedom. When the cage door was opened, neither bird wanted to fly. And so from time to time we called on each other, affording each other the courtesy of a formally arranged visit, ironically now each mistrusting one's own, not the partner's motives, fearing it was only selfish loneliness and hurt that gave reason to meet.

I dreaded the approach of that first Christmas apart, and tried desperately to be 'sensible'. If armies could call a truce at such time, them most certainly I could see no reason for not so doing. The next time he called or phoned as he did frequently, I would tell him that if he had nothing more exciting planned, we could all have lunch together.

I was at first stunned by the blow to my pride, and then relieved, when he said he did have other plans. At least now I could stop feeling anxious about him, but nevertheless resorted to a sleeping pill that night to spare myself the torture of conjecture. However, the following evening we found a note saying that he had reconsidered and it would be a great idea after all to share the Christmas meal - but we were to go home and *he* would cook while I put my feet up! Minty laughed when I told her.

"But Daddy can't cook - he always burns every thing..... and it's comfy here," she added leaving no doubt as to her preferred location for a very important meal. "I'll tell him when I go on Saturday," she decided.

For me, eating a burnt meal was a minor problem beside the one of physically going back home, for I knew I would not find the mental courage to leave a second time. All that I loved and valued: people, sentimental treasures, my books and pictures, were within those walls, and the sight of them would reduce my resolve to shreds. For Minty, the problem was in reverse, for her personal treasures were now here in the cottage, and she wanted them around her at Christmas. In an attempt to reduce the impact of leaving, I had endeavoured to move her like a little snail - with house intact. Indeed I came to be amazed over the years how capable she was of being transplanted, as long as her little world went with her - much as moving a favourite rosebush, carefully resituating the roots and surrounding them with familiar soil before adding daily care and observation.

And so, because the time was not yet, if indeed it might ever feel right - we had once had a good marriage, and I would not want to return for one that was second best - Minty and I ate at the cottage, and Bob at a hotel. I expect we each derived little joy, for if the truth were known, I had set my heart on his joining us for Christmas lunch.

Despair was very close, and the vulnerability it caused, a daily hazard to my equilibrium.

"What a mess," was all I could think as I tossed in my lonely bed, unable to sleep, and all the time wondering if Bob too was awake. If he were, he'd be listening to the World Service, which I couldn't pick up on my radio. The quiet of the night was interminable. Sleep, when it finally came was sheer luxury, but all too soon it was ended by the strident ringing of the alarm that warned me it was time to face another day, and the urge to ignore it and pretend there was no need to go to work, was strong indeed. But, of course, there was every need; the most immediate being to pay the rent and garage bill for the car repairs. Cruelly it seemed that after being trouble free for the fifteen years I had had the Citroen, she now developed every mechanical ailment imaginable.

Christmas proved to be a watershed, and once past, the course of events changed. The experiences and influences we had had on each other could never be completely wiped out, and certainly a shared life could not be destroyed merely by walking away from it. But walk away I had, and quite inexplicably the visiting stopped, and for a long time it looked as though the parting of our ways was inevitable. For many months the distance grew, and commensurately, the pain and misery. It was as if we must make a clean break in order to achieve the amicable partnership that would be necessary if we were to obtain divorce without the trauma and damage that would ensue if we were still emotionally attached. Which of course, we were.

Because I had been the one to leave, Bob eventually seemed to feel challenged to prove he could survive without us. And once the initial angry and hurt reactions subsided and lost their razor sharpness, he almost professionally set about proving exactly that, and made such a convincing job of it that he not only began, quite obviously, to feel more positive, but enjoyed his new freedom from the marriage stakes.

He went to town for concerts and theatre, invited colleagues home for bridge, and played squash vehemently, often apparently beating men ten years his junior. He hadn't had a challenge for some years now, and obviously our absence had presented him with one, and far from being miserable and dejected, he defiantly 'cocked a snoop'. I suppose I envied that freedom and determination not to go under, just as he resented my daily companionship of our daughter.

I began to experience a problem that I had never previously had to face, even in the long periods Bob was away from home when we lived on the Continent, for even then we were in communication. Now I could, and would not, leave Minty to seek out companionship or adult conversation for an hour or so, and longed for Bob's incessant airing of views on every subject under the sun, and for the first time since her birth, I felt trapped.

Not bitterly so, for it was utterly impossible to be with her and feel resentful, but rather I had to learn a practical acceptance of the fact that for someone so special, so precious, one had to pay dearly. And the price of living with a person who did not know the meaning of vanity or selfishness, and who seemed the very embodiment of

191

love itself, was to accept that the commitment was lifelong, and constant. And in that private loneliness, I knew she was as dear to me as life itself.

Such a commitment needed to be shared, yet the need itself an insufficient reason for doing so. In any case, it now seemed to have slipped away as an alternative.

We weathered the winter - literally, and later, when spring came, the view across the half-acre of back garden sloping down to woods more than compensated for the trials of December. The peace afforded by it as I prepared Minty's breakfast, was a very real blessing in those emotionally charged and turbulent days, and I was reluctant to leave it to travel to work. Indeed it was little short of exhilarating, and we could not wait to return each day. I linked with Minty's bus just a quarter of a mile from the cottage, so we invariably came home together.

Except that together wasn't really together any more. Together meant three, and the void just would not disappear.

CHAPTER EIGHTEEN

The passing of March provided an opportunity to move into a less romantic, but easier to manage bungalow, which had also the added advantage of being near to my job, *and* on Minty's bus route. If my car wouldn't start, and there was only once when it didn't, as soon as it was no longer essential, I could walk through the short cuts of the nearby housing estate to school. Conversely the convenience of it gave me time to reflect. Here I had the peace and serenity I had longed for over the past few years; the solitude my broken spirit needed to heal. I began to notice the birdsong; there was a difference about each new morning that my sensibilities appreciated. My mind was sharper, and more receptive to things I had long since failed to notice.

But it was all in a vacuum of loneliness. Often I wondered if Bob had seen the sunrise, or heard the gulls, or noticed the density of the storm clouds, and I knew that a force stronger than any legal vow linked me to him. The threads of our lives had been interwoven for so long that it was almost impossible to separate them. I had made a tear in the fabric - had spoiled it. At best I could leave it torn, or repair it. But it would not be an invisible repair: it would show like a scar, and as such be vulnerable to re-wounding. Outward peace I now had in abundance, and it was all so pointless because of the mental turmoil that raged inside. Just as a weekend is bliss as a respite from the demands of the week, so peace only accrues value when set against the storm.

The surfeit of peace that year was broken only by the attempt to make the second Christmas happier than the first. Bob came to lunch, but he was plainly uncomfortable and on edge at being on 'my patch', and we said goodbye almost formally and with no expressed plan to meet again. More than we realised, Minty was the sticking plaster that held the self-inflicted wound together, for strangely she seemed almost unaffected by the fact that we were no longer under the same roof, openly enjoying the undiluted attention she received when she and Bob were together.

The following Easter, the two of them went off to friends in Wales for a week's holiday. She returned bubbling with news of them, and all they had done; the meals in the garden, the laughing and joking, walking the golf course with Bob, and going fishing for mackerel with Dewi. She had obviously enjoyed the stimulus of happy, noisy company again, and I realised I must encourage her to bring more friends home to the bungalow, male as well as female.

"I'll ask Russell," she said as soon as I put the suggestion to her. "He enjoyed going to the theatre with us."

"I know," I agreed, laughing at the recollection of how he had joined in familiar melodies almost as loudly as the cast. "I'll give you a note for his father and he can come out on the coach with you. And if he'll stay the night, no-one needs to come and collect him, and he can travel back to the Centre with you tomorrow."

But though he ate his tea with undisguised relish, laughed uproariously at only mildly amusing television programmes, nothing in the world would prevent him from returning to base for his sleep.

"I like my bed," he pronounced as if he were in his dotage. "Your pillows wouldn't be the same!"

And no matter how often he came, the ritual followed the same pattern. The girls didn't seem to have the same problem, and the giggling, and talk of boyfriends (largely imaginary) continued long into the night.

One evening the phone rang, and I recognised the voice of one of the young men who had been to several of Minty's parties.

"Could I come and have tea with you please?" He asked very politely, but with that same endearing lack of subtlety that I associated with my daughter.

We fixed the following Thursday, and stepping off the coach, he greeted me warmly, handing Minty his bag to hold while he hugged me. This was not quite what we had expected and she looked perplexed.

"Come in. I expect you two would like to play some records whilst I get tea," I suggested.

"Alright," he agreed, looking around the kitchen as he took off his coat. "Will tea be very long? I'm looking forward to your cooking."

Being assured he would be eating within the hour, off they went to accompany the songs from Oklahoma. "I'm going to get a surrey with a fringe on top for Minty," he called to me. "Would you like to come too?"

By nine o'clock, I was exhausted. He had offered in turn to come and be our protector - (for he was a large well built fellow) - the gardener - pointing out trees in need of felling and a lawn that would be more use as a vegetable plot. Then applying his attention to our lack of a male indoors, assured me he was very good at 'fixing the tele'. He produced a screwdriver from his pocket.

"I'll have the back off in no time!" he announced confidently. Somehow we managed to convince him that it was functioning quite well, and as it was a rented one, we really didn't have to do our own repairs.

"You could do with a man around the place," and he nodded sagely, as if confirming his own suggestion.

He packed away an enormous supper and chatted non-stop for the next hour or so. Minty looked as jaded as I felt. "I think I'll have an early night," she announced.

"I'll just chat to your Mum then." John was not in the least offended by her early disappearance from the scene. Poor old thing; the evening had not been the unmitigated success she had hoped for.

By eleven my eyelids were drooping whilst he continued to effervesce. Reminding him that we both had to get up early in the morning, he agreed to go to his room, but asked if I'd mind if he watched a late night film until he was tired.

I didn't intend to drop off until I'd heard him put out his light, but I must have done, for I was awoken by a gentle tapping at my door. He was apologetic at having to disturb me, but hunger pains were preventing him from sleeping! Wearily I struggled into my dressing gown, and we tiptoed downstairs to make sandwiches.

"I heard ever such a good joke the other day....shall I tell it to you," he offered.

In the circumstances I fancied my chances of getting back to bed at a reasonable hour were greater if I agreed, than not. As it was, he couldn't remember the punch line, so after we made a guess at it, he reverted to a more serious subject.

"Actually, I've got something very important to ask you," he said, tucking into his ham roll.

"Fire away. You've got five minutes and then it's back to bed!"

"Well it's this." He paused sufficiently to herald a significant statement. "How do you fancy me for a son-in-law?"

He was in deadly earnest, so I discreetly hid my smile. "Have you asked Minty?"

"I thought I'd ask you first. You see, we'd need to stay with you! But you are a pretty good cook, so I could cope with living here."

Promising him that the conversation would be resumed at breakfast, I eventually persuaded him that sleep had certain advantages.

He appeared six hours later with the same verve and bounce he had displayed since arriving. He gave me a knowing nudge, spread butter thickly over his toast, and told Minty to prepare for a shock. She looked up from her cornflakes disinterestedly, but waited politely for him to continue. Grinning, he dramatically fell to his knees by her chair. "Will you marry me?"

She looked at him steadily for a moment or two, before resuming the more important business of eating. "No thank you," she said.

I prepared myself for some reaction, but none came. The rejected suitor ladled out some more marmalade and announced that he'd just have to think of someone else to go to tea with!

Since we had moved to the bungalow, the coach had dropped Minty off at the front door, which simplified matters in that I was no longer tied to a specific time to be at an appointed place. Arriving home just ahead of her ensured that I could have a cup of tea waiting, for her day was long, and the journey made more tiring by the numerous stops entailed en route. She was last but one to be delivered, and was rarely home before 5.30; even later when the bus had to wind its way through traffic and Christmas or Sale shoppers to the homes of those living in the city.

We always had ten minutes or so chat when she came home, about our respective days; it had become even more of an essential ritual than it had been when the whole family poured in after each day at work and school: precious private family time when we hoped no-one would come calling. I could see through the window as she alighted from the coach, that she was crestfallen. As always her greeting was warm, but tonight she kept her arm around me a little longer.

"It's hard, isn't it?" she sighed wistfully, "finding the right fella." We sat down at the kitchen table, and I poured her some tea.

"Sometimes impossible, love." I nodded a smile, my lips closed. It was important this one.

"I *do* like John but...." She couldn't articulate her feelings.

"He *was* a handful, wasn't he?" I helped her out. Then she took *me* by surprise. "Like Daddy," she added, and I wasn't sure whether this was her explanation of why our marriage had become unmanageable, or an observation of Bob's untiring energy whenever he had a bee in his bonnet.

It was so tempting to shelter her from the truth by assuring her that Mr. Right would come along one of these days, but it would have been cruel too. So I steered the conversation around to friends we knew who had never married, or had divorced.

"Sometimes it's better to be on your own, you know, than with someone who makes you unhappy."

"Even if you still love them?" Ouch. I didn't know if the bull's-eye was intended, or whether her instinct was making more impact on this conversation than my reason.

"I might marry John if he quietens down a bit," she said reflectively.

I would need more than a cup of tea to enable me to come to terms with that idea, I decided!

At twenty-six, she was in this, as in other ways, ageing prematurely, and possibly seeking to accept what a number of people do when they fear life is passing them by - settle for companionship with anyone who is compatible rather than the rest of a lifetime of loneliness. And lonely she certainly was. Though Jon visited frequently, and Neil whenever he was back in the U.K., and she still saw a great deal of Bob and Aunts and Uncles, none was a substitute for that special relationship that is engendered in a marriage: the total familiarity with just one other person. We had been able to help her resolve every other problem she had ever encountered in her young life, but this was one in which we were powerless.

We could do nothing about the despair of failing to attract a mate. Looking at her sad, shortsighted eyes, I knew why people went on tying the knot despite the divorce rate and misery of broken marriage. We are not equipped to be alone; inbuilt is a basic need, one of another.

"Pet, just supposing you are one of those special people who are brave enough to manage without someone else." What a hash I was making of it! Why couldn't I find the right words? "Is there something else you'd like that would be nearly as nice as getting married....a special holiday maybe? A *really* special one?"

"Holidays only last for two weeks." There was a pause, and then, "Couldn't you find someone for both of us?"

I turned to check the meal cooking in the oven. Silently I conceded she had won this one handsomely on points.

CHAPTER NINETEEN

At Whitsun, Minty and I rented a cottage in the same village as the one belonging to our Wales-based friends. It was make or break time, and I was determined to 'pick myself up, dust myself down', and probably settle for just keeping my head above water. Bill and Joan were the most marvellous therapy, and I understood why Bob had returned feeling stronger. They did not commiserate or take sides, or even offer advice. They were just there.

In their wisdom, they helped me, as they must have helped him, not to do, or decide, or formulate plans, but to find the courage to come to terms with who and what I was. They were the people with whom he would have opened up as with no others, but they gave little away. And irritating though it was, I knew they would have afforded me the same consideration had Bob appeared after my departure.

There was no deliberate tact or sympathy, and we shared experiences of past months as we always did when meeting. With them I learned to laugh again, and for short periods, emptied my mind of that which had obsessed it for so long. But it wasn't the same: the laughter wasn't as noisy or full-blooded as when Bob had been there, and Bill had lost his rival for the most acute observations of human nature. We sat beside their pond until well after dusk, delaying one after another departure with a further anecdote. It was their company that had enticed us to Wales again and again. Indeed I could not imagine this part of the world without them. We had planned to retire here, being unable to imagine anything more pleasurable than being their neighbours.

Minty went inside to borrow one of Joan's cardigans, and I seized the moment to ask just one question, desperately trying to conceal the importance I would attach to their answer.

"Did Bob seem to miss our marriage?"

"Like his right arm," Bill replied dryly as if he were commenting that it looked as if it might rain. And, as if he wished he had diverted the question, added, "but then, that's what you'd expect after twenty-five years. It's a long time. It'll take some getting over for both of you." He broke his rule about not giving advice." You've gone so far, you'll have to give it a bit longer now or there's a danger one of you will go back for the wrong reasons."

I suspected he wouldn't believe it was already twenty months. In normal circumstances, one tends to underestimate the speed with which time passes.

"We're very fond of you," said Joan, for whom Bill was a second husband. "I'm not sure you've got what it takes to bust-up a marriage."

The two statements seemed unconnected so I supposed there were many thoughts she had left unspoken, but I knew better than to press her to elaborate. Besides, she had said the only thing that I had not yet been honest enough to acknowledge, that it might already be too late.

The days flew past, but the change had been even better than the proverbial rest. We lunched with Bill and Joan, and having done all the necessary checks before embarking on a long journey in an old car, it only remained to hope that old age itself wouldn't cause her to expire before the seven-hour drive was over.

We were used to staying in the slow lane, and watching other cars go past, and were determined to make the journey not a chore, but a final part of our holiday. We timed it so that we wouldn't hit London in the rush hour. But our little Busy Lizzie had other ideas; she had done enough to merit her place in the family history book. It was a busy holiday period, and we had to wait a long time for the A.A. man to come. With no radio, and not a restaurant for miles, the wait was tedious indeed.

"I think that's sorted the trouble out," the tired mechanic assessed the situation. "If you have any more bother, give us another call - only it won't be me," he laughed. "I'm just on my way home, thank the Lord. It's been a day and a half."

It was a day and a half for us too - literally, for within the hour, I was trudging to the nearest call box, by which time it was raining in torrents. It was already eight o'clock. Minty slept on the back seat as we prepared for a long wait. A smell of scorching came from under the bonnet.

"'Fraid your clutch has burned out," the next mechanic told me. "Have you got relay?" I handed him my card, and when finally the car was hoisted onto the trailer, we clambered into the cab.

"You look all in," he said kindly. "Why don't you take a leaf out of your daughter's book, and nod off. I've got all your details."
Despite trying to resist the urge to sleep, I eventually succumbed. We stopped to pick up another breakdown, and were not even on the outskirts of London yet. Only when he switched off the engine and tapped on my shoulder did I rouse.

"You're home."
I blinked, and looked about for the familiar street lamp outside the bungalow, but all was darkness. We were in the drive of Three Farthings.

"I'm so terribly sorry...this isn't where I live."

"It's the address on the card luv." It was now 2a.m. I couldn't blame him for his exasperation.

"I've forgotten to get it changed. I used to live here."

"O.K. Where next?" he sighed.

"It's just over three miles down the road...on the edge of the new town."

"Well I suppose that's something. I thought you were about to tell me I should have driven to John O'Groats."

The knowledge that we were so near caused his irritation to subside, and he manoeuvred out onto the road again and Minty who had become expert at smoothing over brittle situations, promised him a mug of tea. As we pulled up at traffic lights, I saw, in his wing mirror, a green Renault behind us.

There was a time when Bob would have slept through the presence of an enormous A.A. truck with amber lights flashing in his garden.

"Helen, what happened? You came home and I didn't hear you knocking." Leaping out of his car, the words all came out in a tumble.

"Funny, she didn't seem to think she lived there," the A.A. man felt compelled to interject.

I put the kettle on whilst the driver off-loaded the car.

"I'll just get Minty to bed and then I'll explain," I promised. "I'm sorry we woke you up."

Bob put an arm around Minty. "I can't think of two people I'd rather be woken up by."

"Busy Lizzie's dead, Dad," Minty explained, almost falling asleep on her feet.

"Not on your life, sweetheart. We'll fix her, you'll see."

The A.A. man came into the kitchen, and sipped his tea thoughtfully. He seemed bent on solving the mystery of the human drama that confronted him, but Bob kept guiding the conversation back to the car, and in the process obtained a comprehensive picture of the problem. He left us soon after, and with Minty fast asleep, I recounted the saga of our wretched journey home.

"Um, seems you prefer this go-it-alone life."

I could see he was enjoying the upper hand, in addition to having the advantage of at least a few hours sleep.

"Reckon you've got two choices – you'll have to divorce me which will provide you with enough money to get a decent car or...."

"Or what?"

"Invite me to lunch tomorrow, and I'll make a start on it."

"You can come to lunch, but I'll get my own car fixed. I'm not going to be blackmailed."

"We'll see about that! Night."

He left and all I had wanted to do was fall into his arms.

Being Sunday, we couldn't get all the parts that were needed, so Bob came most evenings after school that week. Minty, who hovered on the base line of the situation for a day or two, began to assert herself. Without the advantage of intellect to guide her, she depended solely on intuition, an intuition that with hindsight seems to have been so reliable that I began almost to depend on it. She was my barometer, who accepted that each day brought with it new circumstances. If only we had the courage to live one day at a time, then plans could be adjusted in the light of constant and natural change.

She taught us that if we found ourselves in tune, then living separately need not affect our ability to make the most of that day. We need look no further than the day itself; need not assume that if we joined for an outing, this would automatically mean we had decided to spend the rest of our lives together, for there remained the fear that this might not be the answer. We, as 'normal' adults were much more bound by convention. What would people think? Would we lose credibility? We had been separate now for a long time.

Minty's delight in the day itself provided the answer. What did it matter what other people thought or believed, and in the acceptance of that, we achieved an honesty about our relationship that became so precious that we were hesitant to look further than 'today'.

One evening after she had been to help Dad with the gardening, she returned brimming over with a plan for the following weekend. She and I were to prepare cold chicken and salad: Dad would bring a bottle of wine. They would need a couple of hours on Saturday morning to do something secret, and then we would all go off to 'a big house'.

The long separation had now rid me of the desire to rebel when Bob called the tune of every detail, and I looked forward eagerly to the weekends. The period apart had not been totally futile. Even though the reason had nearly always been to push all other thoughts from my mind, I had learned to take time to write. I felt stronger and more of an individual. I discovered how much there was to life that I had failed to notice whilst allowing the misery of argument to consume me. There was a whole world outside the bitterness of a marriage under threat. But there was guilt too, and it was tearing me apart. I had found the courage to make the initial break, but not the courage to sustain it. I did not know why this was so, but I was soon to find out.

In story-book fashion, the following Saturday dawned bright and full of promise. Minty and Bob went off on their secret mission, and once accomplished I was collected, and we drove off to Penshurst Place, somewhere I had expressed a wish to visit several years ago, and which, in the general way of things, we never did. Minty lapped up the gentleness of spirit between us; we laughed, we sang, and made absolutely no attempt to disguise the sheer joy of being a threesome

. It was no use pretending any more, for the realisation crystallised in each of us that afternoon, that the long separation would soon be over. Not that we were blind to the fact that it would never be a smooth passage to old age, but the chemistry would not be denied. And in the manner of it being better to travel than arrive, we savoured every precious minute of it. All through the chicken and salad, Minty repeated "and you don't know our secret Mum."

"But she will if you give her many more clues," Bob chided her affectionately.

We hadn't noticed an elderly couple sitting nearby, or that we were providing them with entertainment. Like a young couple finding love for the first time we hadn't noticed very much at all!

With a great sense of ceremony a large plastic container was opened to reveal the season's first strawberries and a carton of cream to satisfy a family of six! Minty looked up at me to receive the long awaited expression of surprise and delight, which I duly produced, having studiously avoided looking at her red-stained hands when she came to collect me! But it was a comment from the old lady to her husband that caused our greatest delight of all. She spoke in a loud voice as the elderly, slightly deaf, often do. "Ee Dad, yer can tell they're not married, can't yer?"

And with those words, the bleakest chapter of our lives had come to a close.

"We'll have a blessing in Church - the wedding we didn't have in Canada. This time we're on the same side of the Atlantic as all our family. And I'll drive you to church in a pony and trap...."

"Through the village!" I said aghast.

"Yep, and I'll bring you white roses for all the world to see."
I smiled to myself, imagining how Neil and Jon would curl up with sheer embarrassment at the very thought of all this.

"And I shall be a bridesmaid again!" Minty interrupted my thoughts. They were having such fun the pair of them that I hadn't the heart to protest - at least not yet!

We were determined to plan it all carefully so that no pressure could ruin our reconciliation. Bob wanted to paint the outside of the house. Minty and I would return in the summer holiday. We sat in the little bungalow garden a long time that evening, listening to the call of the river birds, and dreaming. Hours passed before I could sleep. I went over and over the events of the day as one plays a favourite record. We had slipped into a decision as naturally as into a bathrobe. What if we were just heading for a re-run of the problem years....or had we really learned to value each other for better or worse. It was really of no consequence, because being back at base was all that mattered and nothing was going to keep us apart. I hugged my pillow and allowed the months of putting on a brave face to dissipate into tears of joy.

CHAPTER TWENTY

Dawn was just breaking when I was awoken by the strident ringing of the telephone.   For someone to be calling at this hour, it could only be an emergency. My parents.......they were well into their seventies now. Oh please no. Neil....Jon...an accident.

"Yes? Who?"

The voice on the other end was both strained and strange, but whoever it was knew my name "Heln....Heln..."

"Bob, is that you? Whatever's wrong? You've been drinking...."

"No. Come"

The line was dead. If he hadn't been drinking, then he had been attacked, burgled perhaps. The voice had been so weak.

Throwing a coat over my nightclothes, not stopping to change from slippers, I rushed out and threw myself into the car. Dear old thing, she started first time. Bob had done a good job on her, and only the fact of her being an old lady, and the journey uphill, prevented us from breaking the speed limit.

What a relief; as he had frequently done in the past, he had forgotten to lock the door. I rushed through the kitchen, and had one foot on the stairs when the sound of my name from the lounge told me that he was still by the phone. Thank goodness he had managed to get downstairs to call me: he might have been lying there for hours unable to get help. The thoughts that sped through my mind were unbearable. And then I realised that he hadn't been to bed...too happy to go to sleep, he told me afterwards. He had worked on a translation, and now here he was, the person who yesterday had been so strong and carefree, slumped and weakened in our 'story' chair.

One glance at his distorted face told me he had had a stroke. Hugging and comforting him, I wrapped a blanket around his shoulders and called an ambulance. How stupid of me not to have dressed - I could have driven him to the hospital myself. But then if something happened on the way... No it was better like this. Except that nothing worse *must* happen on the way. With help, he could stand, but his arm felt stiff. We waited for the ambulance in silence, wanting nothing more than to be together.

"When the it comes, I'll go and explain to Minty, and then come to you. I'll ask Margaret if she can stay with her. I'll be there before they've finished examining you. Just be strong until I get there. Everything's going to be all right. Keep thinking about strawberries and cream, and how perfect yesterday was. There are going to be lots of days like that."

The ambulance was in the drive now, and two men were approaching the house with a wheelchair.

"Don't forget - strawberries and cream."

As the ambulance pulled out into the road, I swiftly looked about me. I had been catapulted back into the home we had built together. Bob's Russian books were strewn around the armchair just as I remembered them before. He was an untidy so-and-so - everything all over the place. But it didn't matter. Nothing mattered any more. It would all be so pointless if...But I would not contemplate the 'if.' I looked about for the house keys before locking up. They would be in his jacket pocket from yesterday.

From the bedroom window I could see the hole where there had once been an almond tree and wondered if the people who owned the cottage ever noticed they had got an extra one. My photograph was on the dressing table..... I checked the immersion was off as if I had never been away, detached the kettle plug from the socket, and then went out into the early morning sunshine. All the way back, I failed to convince myself that it wasn't some ghastly nightmare.

My neighbours' curtains were still drawn - of course they were; it was not yet seven o'clock on Sunday morning. I made Minty a breakfast tray, and then woke her and explained that Dad hadn't been feeling well in the night, and I must ask the doctor about him; a somewhat watered down version of the truth but the best I could muster. I would leave a note in Margaret's letter box, and then phone her from the hospital. Could my girl be very grown-up, and stay safe until I came home again?

She assured me she would - had I forgotten she was twenty six - and like a very sensible grown-up, she would go back for a lie in! And hadn't it all been fun yesterday? Would I ask Dad if we could do it all again next week?

But I couldn't ask Dad anything, because he slept deeply for many hours. I returned to the bungalow to check all was well, and found Minty happily dusting, having packed half a dozen jigsaw puzzles in a box.

"These are to take to Three Farthings," she explained, "for when we have rainy days there again."

Rainy days...any kind of days...but just let there be days ahead for us. Margaret called to say not to worry, Minty could spend the day with them...I could go back to the hospital for as long as was needed.

"I'll go now then," I said gratefully. "Help yourself to coffee."

She had already put the kettle on, and was taking three cups from the cupboard.

"You'll have one too before you go," she commanded. "And then Minty here can come and help me cook Sunday lunch."

"Thanks. I'll drink it while I make a couple of calls."

Though lying down when I arrived the second time, he was wide awake. There was not a shred of self-pity: only a characteristic determination to get over another hurdle.

"Bit like being in business again - you never know where the next blow is coming from!" He had attempted to make light of it, but his voice caught on the last word, and he swallowed hard. "Bit of a blinder though, wasn't it?"

I squeezed his hand; it was cold and unresponsive.

"Rub my fingers, Helen. Keep rubbing."

I did as he asked but I knew from his face there was no feeling.

"Are you rubbing?"

I nodded. "What else can I do?" Sheer inadequacy prompted me to ask, "Has the physio been?" I forgot it was Sunday.

"Coming tomorrow, the doctor says. I just have to rest today."

"You rest and I'll rub your fingers." It seemed such a childish response; something for each of us to do to help the situation along.

"Does Minty know?"

"I just told her you weren't well. I didn't really stop to think it through. I'll explain when I go home. I've left messages for Jon and Neil."

"Good lass. Rub some more."

I hadn't stopped, but I said. "O.K. I'm going to wiggle one finger at a time."

"Bit old for 'This little pig went to market' aren't I ?"

We joked, but tears came more readily than laughter.

"Minty enjoyed yesterday. She asked me to tell you."

"What about you?"

"Heaven. Best day of all. Weren't the old couple funny?"

"A riot. Let's stay not married. It's much more fun."

"Alright, I'll come back to Three Farthings and live in sin with you."

"Idiot." And I knew from his expression that he thought he was squeezing my hand.

We stayed like that for a long time. At least the movement of the fingers had made them warmer. He fell asleep and I looked about me. Such a bleak Victorian room with its high ceiling and gloss paint. The faded curtains hung limply from the rail; some of the hooks had come adrift causing the folds to hang unevenly, and balls of collected dust were visible at the back of the radiator. From the window could be seen the scaffolding and building supplies in preparation for a new wing that was planned ultimately to take the place of this old sanatorium section. Pity it was being neglected even before it had gone out of use.

I put the pyjamas I had been hard pressed to find, in the locker. Tomorrow I'd go out and get him some new ones. Hanging the towels on the rail at the back of the bedside cabinet, I saw the earphones had fallen on the floor, and bending to pick them up discovered whoever cleaned the room must have had tunnel vision, because whatever dust failed to come within a radius of arm's length seemed to have been ignored.

The door was suddenly pushed open, and a silent orderly lethargically placed cutlery and cruet on the mobile bed-table, and then withdrew without a word. I could hear nurses approaching with the dinner trolley.

"Roast beef or salad?" one of them called from the corridor, before popping her head around the door.

"I don't think he's too bothered. He's very sleepy. Perhaps if you leave salad, and then he can have it when he wakes up," I said.

"Right you are - one salad coming up."

The doctor came round soon afterwards - a young houseman with whom I knew Bob would get on. "The sleep is doing him a power of good - he may not wake for another few hours. There's a good film on in the day room, if you feel like a break."

I thanked him and said that in the circumstances I'd go home and return in the evening. The lettuce leaves were beginning to look as limp as the curtains, and I nibbled a piece of the hard-boiled egg before whispering to Bob that I'd be back. He didn't hear me.

When I reached the bungalow, Ken, Margaret's husband, came out to tell me that Jon had rung to say he was at the hospital, and Neil would be there soon and perhaps it would be better if I didn't go back until tomorrow. So we sat in the garden, and I explained that Dad would be in hospital for a while; that I'd need to go and visit each day. I didn't go into detail, so when Minty said, 'I expect he ate too many strawberries, and his tummy is none too pleased,' I smiled in agreement.

"When I come home from the Centre, if I don't see Busy Lizzie in the drive, I'll go into Ken and Margaret's. They told me to do that."

I whispered a silent thanks. What would I have done without them?

Before visiting next day, I phoned to see what the physio had suggested.

"He must practise picking things up," the Nurse said.

"What sort of things? Big... small?"

"Small I think. If you get here before four o'clock, you could have a word with her."

I rushed home from school, bundling the end-of-term reports into a briefcase, and filled an empty margarine tub with buttons, screws etc before driving into the city. I glanced at the dashboard. Three fifty. Ten minutes, ten miles. Parking and getting up to the second floor of the hospital consumed precious time, and I just missed her.

"It doesn't matter," Bob said wearily. "She says I won't be going to physio until tomorrow. They are going to see if I can dip a paintbrush into separate colours."

He smiled when I opened the plastic carton. "I might have known teacher would want to get started right away."

"Give me your hand," I said gently, immediately wanting to bite my tongue. How could I have been so thoughtless when his arm was totally unresponsive to his attempt to raise it.

"You'll have to help yourself love. C'mon, it's not the end of the world. We'll beat it together eh?"

He used his unaffected hand to place buttons between the fingers of the hand that seemed lifeless, first near the knuckle and then by the tips. He suddenly became alert.

"I felt it! I felt the button! But I can't tell which finger."

He thrilled to that tiny hope, and we continued manipulating until he began to feel tired again. By the end of the week, signs of life were returning to his left hand.

"I'm to go on the scanner soon. The consultant's pretty pleased. I've been up all afternoon and I'm not a bit tired."

"Minty's coming tomorrow," I told him.

"Great. Thanks for delaying it."

"She has never seen you ill. She'll be pleased to know you'll soon be home."

"That's why it was such a shock. Being so fit explains why I've recovered quickly."

A 'one-off' was the verdict after two weeks in hospital. Bob could go home and slowly ease his way back into a normal lifestyle. The consultant did not expect to see him again. But patience was never Bob's strong point.

"Never mind slowly," he grimaced. "I want to be playing cricket again before the end of the season. Right now I'm going home to finish that decorating - normal service will be resumed as soon as possible!"

"Right now," I said, taking the reins for the first time, "you are going to rest. And home is where Minty and I are. There will be no argument or I shall refuse to come and collect you. Come to think of it, I've enjoyed driving your car!"

He agreed like a shot to come back to the bungalow. "Thanks, "I'll do the cooking and housework while you're at school, to earn my keep!"

"I couldn't cope with quite that much reformation overnight: it would be too great a shock to the system. You just put your feet up and watch the Test Match!"

But he had the last word. He was playing cricket by the end of the season. And there were no words to describe his elation on the evening he took not one, but two catches.

"OK. Bob, talk us all through it." His friend Bernard had come back to the bungalow, closely followed by Jack and Andy, for a celebration drink.

"You have to admit fellas, the second one was inspired!" There was no mistaking the sheer pleasure he had experienced.

"It *was* actually," Bernard whispered. "And so is his rate of recovery." And then to Bob "Um, not bad for an old un!" They talked until late, reminiscing over various matches, happily relaxed with the weekend ahead.

Next morning Bob appeared in a tracksuit. And as I had been afraid it might, the cricket match success had gone to his head. I thought hard before saying anything, and he wandered off to find his trainers. Minty saw I was worried. " I'll go with him Mum - slow him down a bit."

"I'm not at all certain he's going to be slowed down pet. If he thinks he's back on form, there'll be no stopping him."
He was in the kitchen before I finished my sentence.

"I'm sorry you two, but I was jogging for twenty years before this damn brain haemorrhage, and the most satisfying part was when I pushed myself through the pain barrier. I know I've never convinced you how much easier it is to face the day when you have pushed your body to its limit - completely empty your mind of its problems, step right outside them, and you can handle anything."

"I'm not sure you are ready to handle *anything,"* I protested. "Why won't you be patient?"

"Helen, I can't go in for this 'gentle jog-around-the-block' business just to keep in trim. That's for middle-aged ladies who suddenly realise they are getting stiff."

"Point taken!" I responded weakly, not wishing to be argumentative.

"You're not a middle-aged lady."

"I most certainly am."

"I've never categorised you, and I won't start now. Try to understand that I'm fit and well again - If I can't do the things I enjoy most, then I'll throw in the towel."
He looked at me for agreement, and he didn't know that my nod indicated an acceptance, not only of his words, but of the fact that life with us was still not quite enough: just to be well and here was insufficient. There had to be much more; enough to take him to the pain barrier, and beyond, as he had said. 'Love is to Man a thing apart....' Alexander Pope certainly knew all about human nature.

"Will anything I say make the least difference?"
He lifted my chin, for my eyes were downcast to hide the fear I did not wish him to see.

"I guess if you threatened to leave me again, I'd give in, but then I'd be a bear to live with until I'd done it, you know that."

"Just one thing - wait for five minutes and ask yourself if it's wise."

"Did that in bed."
He walked away, as if momentarily persuaded to another point of view, which was unnerving because that was so uncharacteristic; despite the relief it afforded me. And then he turned and said in decisive tones which brooked no argument, "Helen I've played cricket with no after effect.......alright so I haven't managed squash yet. But I have to know for myself that I'm really as fit as I feel."
I made one last attempt. "Can I be selfish and tell you I'd quite like to have you around for awhile. Be patient - let the hospital give you your answer."

"They didn't put me on the scanner. The consultant was so pleased with the speed of my recovery, I guess he felt there was no need."

I suspected that Bob thought otherwise, and wanted, as I certainly did, to know what the scanner might have indicated; hence the urge now to put himself to the test.

Minty appeared in her tracksuit.

"I see you're as stubborn as your father," I said with amused resignation.
Bob patted her head. "But if I go ahead, you come back to Mum."
Just looking like a jogger for ten minutes, albeit a very solid one, was enough, and having gone through the motions, she was soon home.

"Dad's alright – he's ever so happy," she assured me. "He says he's going as far as the river."

"Stupid oaf," I muttered to myself. But he was right - he would never accept a half-life. I just hoped that what he was finding out about himself right now was that he was still as tough as old boots!

I had drunk two cups of coffee before he came panting and sweating through the door. He put a hand on each of my shoulders. "Will you settle for life beginning at fifty?"

Term at last came to an end, and we planned a summer holiday of doing just the amount of gardening and outside painting at Three Farthings that could be coped with under the umbrella of fun. We had been given a warning to value each day rather than use them as a race against time. What we didn't know was that there were to be so few of those days.

CHAPTER TWENTY ONE

This time, the stroke, which happened just after I had gone to bed, leaving Bob to watch a film, was worse. Having learned to sleep lightly, I heard him walk awkwardly through the sitting-room door to the hall.

"It's happening again - the sensation in my arm." And then he crumpled to the floor. I put a pillow beneath his head, and looking up saw Minty in the doorway of our bedroom. I could not protect her from it as I had done before and so it seemed kinder to involve her.

"Put a blanket over Daddy, love, whilst I phone for some help. Then put all the lights on in front of the house so the driver can see where we are."

The wheelchair that first appeared was quickly discarded in favour of a stretcher, and with Bob safely taken care of I dressed quickly, and asked Minty if she could be very brave and sleep until morning whilst I followed the ambulance in the car. Before she could reply, Ken, who had been watching the same film, and had seen the ambulance arrive, was on the doorstep.

"She can come and sleep on our couch."
They went out together and I locked the door.

It was dawn before examinations were over, and with Bob again deeply asleep, he was taken from casualty to the ward.

"It's alright. He isn't going to die," assured a young doctor. "Yes, he's had another stroke, but it's not as bad as it looks. Go home now." and come back later today

216

I didn't go direct to the bungalow, but stopped at Three Farthings. I made some strong coffee and sipped it in the secure comfort of the story chair. Dear old refuge: there was little it didn't know about us all. I looked around the room: There was no part of this house that didn't have a memory. The stone archway, above which trim plaster now concealed a huge girder that had taken the strength of two young families to heave into place. I recalled our boys, and cousin Michael, all wearing short pants then, positioned at different levels on the stairs holding on to a rope wound round the newel post, while Bob and Uncle Mike struggled with the sheer weight and awkwardness of getting the brute into position. And I knew behind the picture that Joan from Wales had painted for us, was an uneven bit of wall where there had previously been a dining hatch. An old range where the coats now hung had provided warmth before Bob put in central heating. And where I was sitting, we once stacked all the new window frames that replaced the metal ones.

I sat for a long time. This would never be just a house, and one day, God willing, we'd be back here.

Totally accepting the doctor's assurance, I took Minty with me to the hospital later, fully expecting to see Bob looking brighter, as on the previous occasion. With the pyjamas, we even packed the box of buttons. The shock of finding him comatose, and sweating profusely dulled my brain. We sat on either side of him, mopping him with a towel until it too was wringing wet, and Minty put her hands lightly on his face. Her voice was barely audible. "Dad's going to die, Mummy."

"No Minty, no." I whispered, even though her voice contained more authority than that of the doctor the night before.

There cannot be many hours that are longer than those waiting for someone to regain consciousness. I changed his pyjamas twice in the next hour, but it was a pointless exercise, because the sheets were in a similar state, and no-one seemed to be remotely interested. A visitor at the next bedside told me that Sister was in her office. I nodded my thanks wondering why I hadn't been to find her before.

"Minty, stay by Dad. I won't be long." But it had all been too much for her.

"I'll come with you," she said.

The visitor got up again. "I'll sit with him."

"I'm very grateful. I'll try not to be long."

"Take all the time you need. Somebody ought to be doing something."

The office door was open, and Sister was on the phone. Since she neither beckoned to acknowledge she had seen me, nor give any indication that I was to wait, I paced up and down sufficiently near the doorway to let her know I hadn't gone away. I heard the receiver being put down. She straightened a few papers, returned her coffee cup to the tray, and said, "Yes, can I help you," with no discernible degree of concern.

"No, but I would be grateful if you would help my husband. I brought him into casualty last night. Has he been comatose since then?"

She ignored the question. "If there were cause for concern, we would let you know."

"I am already concerned. My regret is that nobody else appears to be."

"Doctor will comment when he does the round."

"But when will that be?"

"Before six."

"But that's three hours away. He needs a doctor now."

She smiled condescendingly.....a superior, professional smile. "I said *before* six."

I looked at her squarely, the confrontation unnerving me. "I'm going to take my daughter home, and then I'll be straight back. Please get a doctor now. If he hasn't been attended to by the time I return, I shall make a formal complaint holding you personally responsible."

She implied she was in charge, and competent. But she didn't leave her office.

I bundled Bob's wet pyjamas into a polythene bag, and took Minty to the car. As I left I saw Jon's car speeding up the hospital drive, and though they hadn't travelled together, Bob's best friend was just behind. "Thank God," I breathed.

The phone was ringing as I put my key in the door. It was Jon. "Stay where you are for a while," he urged. It's best you are at the end of a phone. Have something to eat. Minty alright?"

"She will be when I have made her a drink and settled her. Keep in touch." There's nothing more precious than family when things are badly wrong.

It was late evening when the Sister phoned to tell me that Doctor had seen Bob, and was concerned, and that he would be transferred to The London Hospital in Whitechapel. My son had left to collect me, and should be with me very soon.

We were ready at the door when Jon arrived. Dropping Minty off at Ken and Margaret's, we nevertheless reached the London Hospital seconds after the ambulance, to be told that unless Bob had an operation immediately, the massive haemorrhage would kill him. It was almost ten now; it would take about three hours. We could sleep in the visitors' room. Jon, who as a policeman had spent many such nights, had soon prevailed upon a nurse to show him where the teabags were, and together we passed those desperate hours. Two o'clock came and went as did three and four. It had all taken so long because in removing the haemorrhage from the brain, they had found a tumour, the tumour that must have caused not only this, but the first stroke.

It was a further four hours, at 8am, when we learned that he had survived the delicate operation but he was not out of the woods yet. An exhausted surgeon took me aside. In the next few hours I must accept that the brain damage may cause my husband to be a vegetable. He had bled for a very long time having lain for almost a whole day virtually unattended by our local hospital. My head would absorb no more and I shook it disbelievingly. The doctor touched my hand gently. "It may not be so bad but be prepared."

"My daughter is already handicapped." I said, not as a protest, but because of the association of ideas, and his placing of my thoughts on that particular track. He obviously thought I was complaining about the unfairness of it, and said only, "I am so very sorry."

Towards mid-day, the anaesthetic was at last wearing off.

"I want you to ask your husband who the Prime Minister is," the consultant instructed. "He is more likely to respond to your voice than mine."

Terrified of the possibility he had presented earlier, my words came out in a high-pitched whisper. I swallowed hard, tried again, and failed. Jon took over, holding his father's hand. Bob didn't open his eyes, but no words could describe the sheer delirium that swept over us as he said scornfully, "Well unless there was a coup last night, it's Margaret Thatcher. What a bloody stupid question!"

The uttering of his answer to that 'bloody stupid question' exhausted him, and he fell asleep. Jon and I hugged each other, as if the past twenty-four hours had made no demand whatsoever on our mental reserves.

"I see we have a character on our hands," the consultant smiled wryly. "Does he have any medical knowledge?"

"There's not much he hasn't dipped into," I said mechanically. Looking back I should perhaps have attached more importance to that question, but my mind was totally absorbed by the revelation in those past minutes that he was not, after all, a vegetable. He wasn't even changed; the same acerbic Bob, with his 'very-much-to-the-point' responses. Such economy of words before returning to the task in hand: the process of recovery.

"You go and sleep too now," Sister commanded gently. But our bodies were too taut to relax, and though I experienced an immense mental weariness, Jon's adrenalin was flowing, and he drove us back to tell Minty the good news. We didn't speak much for our minds were racing so fast in recapping the night's events that there seemed no time to interrupt thoughts with comments to each other. In any case they would have been superfluous since we were both retracing the same ground.

Minty reacted in a pleased but very perplexed way; perhaps because she found it hard to equate our apparent relief with the fact that Dad was so ill. Or maybe in our absence she had prepared herself for what she imagined would be the gravest news. We had at various times discussed death; she had seen death on television; pets of hers had died. Even young friends at the Centre had passed on. She understood.

"Is he coming home soon?" she asked.

"No, not for a long time yet. But he can talk, and understand. Isn't that wonderful?"

But Dad had always been able to talk and understand. What did I mean, she must have wondered. A slow sort of consternation filled her eyes but it all seemed too complicated in my tiredness, to explain. And because she was an angel, she didn't press me with 'why' and 'how'. Though she couldn't understand how I could be happy in these circumstances, it was enough that I *was* so, and I went to my room to find she had made the bed and turned back the covers ready for me to rest.

Jon also slept for a while before going home and I woke to find a note to say he'd phone later. The delirium of knowing Bob's mind had been unaffected carried me through the day, but with the passing of the hours I began mentally to collect all the questions I now needed to ask. They had said to phone at any time. Jon, when he went on duty at his station not far from Whitechapel, would look in on Bob, but he must have no more visitors until the next day. Thank goodness I had the school holiday ahead and we could go up to the hospital in London each day. What a luxury only to be required to concentrate on one thing at a time.

Next day we drove the four miles to our nearest railway station and were on the platform ready for the first train. Someone passed very close and smiled; one of the mothers who often came into the school to help.

"Making the most of your holiday?" she asked brightly. "Lovely day - what are you going to do in London?"

I just could not formulate a reply and stared dumbly, at her. She turned to Minty instead. "Have a super time. Must go - my brood are further down the platform."

I felt stunned by my own inability to tell her what had happened. Indeed it was as if in trying to explain, I was only just believing it myself. I continued to stare after her as she gathered her family into a carriage, and saw her glance back at us uncertainly.

We got off at Liverpool Street, and took the tube to Whitechapel. The bleakness of an English Sunday was now replaced by the bustle of the street market, and we threaded our way past the stalls and crossed over to the flight of steps into the hospital. No sooner were we inside the main door than we felt the air of calm competence that pervaded the entire building. After that hour-long exposure to the world, it was all so safe again, and I breathed more easily. Bob had been moved, but was still in Intensive Care, which confused me.

"I thought it was alright now," I said to the first doctor I saw.

Far from giving me the impression that I should have prefaced my question with an introduction or explanation, he asked for neither, but said gently, "If the operation was only done yesterday then we have to keep a close eye for a day or two."

"You mean things can still go wrong?"

"One day at a time?" he smiled. "Come on - you can introduce me."

I looked about for Bob, and eventually saw him only a few feet away. I hadn't expected the turban, and the shaved head, and yet they must have been apparent yesterday. A nurse greeted us warmly..

"Come to help us?" she squeezed Minty's hand. "We could do with an extra nurse."

We felt welcome, and not at all in the way. Indifference had no place here.

"The kitchen's just down the corridor - make coffee whenever you wish. Your husband will need to sleep quite a bit, so you might

222

need a break now and then. And if you want a meal, I'll organise you a pass into the staff canteen," another nurse said.

I presumed upon Minty's patient and gentle nature so much in the next six weeks as each day of that mercifully long summer recess, we boarded the train for London's East End to the hospital in Whitechapel. Most times she came too, enjoying both the journey as it became increasingly familiar, and the lunch breaks with doctors, nurses and porters who all ate in the same canteen.

Most of all she responded wholeheartedly to the ward staff who provided her with simple jobs, and I was reminded of how important it was for her, as with any other human being, to feel needed. This was an aspect of her development to which perhaps we had attached insufficient importance, assuming that it is the handicapped who need help, and in our caring, are oblivious to the fact that their self esteem is increased by virtue of the help they in turn are able to give.

Strange how we complain there are not enough hours in the day to just sit and reflect, only to find time is there for the taking, if only we attach a degree of importance to our reason for doing so. All those demands on my time were insignificant beside the one act of sitting and waiting now for Bob to come off the danger list. As he slept, so I could observe our daughter interacting with other adults. Some days it seemed better that she went to the Centre instead of the hospital - the days that were more distressing and which were better she avoided. Sometimes a lack of intellect provoked the greater imaginings, and there was no doubt that her instinct, rightly or wrongly, was not optimistic.

I could never have imagined the world of difference between a large teaching hospital and the one to which Bob was originally admitted. So professional and compassionate; such meticulous and ungrudging care; such dignity afforded to each patient.

There were many setbacks in those early days whilst he was in Intensive care, meningitis causing an unexpected alarm, but Bob's courage and determination were phenomenal. He fought against the odds every inch of the way. Though he appeared to be as alert as ever, doctors were disappointed in the amount of movement that had returned to his limbs - practically none on the left side, but the physios worked unstintingly, and by virtue of just a hint of the progress that might be achieved, he stayed there for a sixth week.

Here we felt safe: all that could possibly be done was being done. He was the recipient of a combination of the best brains and finest nursing, and I pleaded that he might stay with them but this could not be, and by September he was back in our local hospital, for post-operative care. At least I could visit every day after school. On a good day I could be with him in half an hour, tending to arrive at the end of his physiotherapy session. Instead of returning immediately to the dusty Victorian side ward he occupied alone, we would manoeuvre his wheelchair in the direction of the new wing with its comfy modern WRVS Unit. With lighter hearts and precious time together we would pretend we were by the Seine, watching the crowds and sipping coffee after coffee.

At five o'clock the shutters would go down, and the ladies packed away their displays of chocolate bars and biscuits. Their departure marked the end of our make-believe world, and the roundabout return to the ward cast a gloom for awhile, for back there we entered the routine regime of meals and medicines, temperature charts and doctors' notes... and yet the simultaneous contradiction of a wardrobe thick with dust and uncollected dirty linen. After weeks of visiting, I did not bother to be discreet about cleaning the room myself. Cleaning wasn't a nursing duty, I was told. But surely the supervision of it was? Bob was to be kept free of infection the London Hospital had decreed. They surely would not believe what I saw in those months. Even his urine bottles remained uncollected until, when tact achieved nothing, I did the job myself.

It was as a result of his massive determination and immeasurable courage that against all the odds he was, albeit with the aid of a stick, walking again by November. His doctor was astounded.

But in November, fate was to strike another blow, and I had to tell him that I would not be able to visit for two days because I must travel north for my father's funeral. My brain failed completely to accept this latest crisis for I had never conceived of life without the man who, to four daughters, had been rock and counsellor, and it was some weeks before grief for him enveloped me. Bob's only reaction was simply that he was coming too, and no amount of argument affected his decision. Absolutely adamant, he prevailed upon his consultant, and with a borrowed wheelchair in the boot, Jon drove us through the November mist and drizzle to my parents' home. Neil was abroad, and Minty asked to stay behind with a friend.

Time with grandparents had never been other than pleasurable for her, and she seemed unable to face the sadness that now surrounded them. If she did not want to cloud her memory of her holidays with them, I did not choose to insist otherwise. With my mother and sisters I followed the coffin back down the aisle, and ahead of us were my husband and son, for Jon had pulled the wheelchair to the back of the Church towards the end of the service, to face the cortège. Only one month ago, my father had visited Bob, and wheeled him around the hospital grounds, encouraging and cajoling him. And now he was dead, and I had not had the time to be with him in his brief but final suffering of unsuspected cancer, before, with his lifelong habit of causing no fuss, he had slipped away so quietly.

The funeral had exhausted Bob, and we still had the long journey home. He had sat so quietly amongst the mourners, watching everyone in a detached sort of way, smiling and speaking only when spoken to. Those who knew him well must have found the difference in him so difficult to accept, for always he had been the initiator of conversations, so full of energy and ideas. Helping him to get into his overcoat, and then into the wheel-chair, I heard someone remark what a tragedy it was, and desperately hoped he hadn't heard. This was the half-life he vowed he would never settle for.

He slept for most of the journey, and I whispered to Jon to drive back to the bungalow instead of the hospital. Bob had been coming home for three weekends now, since the ward was closed from Friday until Monday. It made the week so much shorter, and once home we had practised all that he had been taught in the physiotherapy unit, by pushing the furniture to the edge of the room leaving a large area of carpet free. Over and over again he would try to manoeuvre himself from the armchair to wheelchair, from sitting to standing, and from lying to kneeling. The latter was the most difficult; often he would end up in a heap on the floor. But Minty was always there with me to lift uncooperative limbs into position, and to rock Dad gently backwards and forwards until we had him near enough to something solid to lever him up.

And so it surely couldn't harm if we stole one extra night for him to have the comfort of an undisturbed sleep. Between us we got him to bed and propped him up on pillows. With just the gentle bedside lamp on, we all listened to the radio and drank hot chocolate, before Jon left us to go home.

"You're getting very good at making decisions," Bob teased when some of the weariness had disappeared. "I hope you'll tell them tomorrow that it was all your idea!"

"I'll tell them," I promised, "but not until you have had a lie in. You have coped marvellously today. Dad would have been full of admiration for you. Thanks for insisting on coming, but now you must rest."

"I wouldn't have missed saying farewell to the old fellow, but you're right, I'm tired now."

I phoned the physio department at the hospital before he was awake next morning, to explain his absence. Liz, the senior therapist completely understood and said she would have made exactly the same decision. She offered to ring the ward for me, and suggested we came in for the afternoon session at three o'clock. I liked her a great deal, and valued the immense support she had been over the past weeks.

"Are we going to have a coffee together before I go back?" he asked, and I knew how much he hated the thought of returning, but as long as he was making progress in the physiotherapy unit for that one precious hour each day, he would put up with the lack of care on the ward. So often I heard patients even more disabled than Bob, describe their frustration at having their meals hurriedly put down beyond their reach, and then removed an hour later by someone who felt disgruntled they had bothered to bring a meal at all if it wasn't going to be eaten. Friends, particularly ex-nurses, were disgusted at the lack of hygiene and hearing patients' calls going unheeded, whilst young staff, lacking direction and leadership, chatted in the corridor or around the desk.

"We are not only going to have coffee, but lunch as well. Liz says you can have the afternoon session today."

He smiled contentedly. "Three whole hours, and then in two days I'll be back again for the weekend."

We listened to the morning story on the radio and enjoyed a lazy lunch, before battling with coat, wheelchair and car again.

I left him in time for me to meet Minty from her coach. Tomorrow I would be back at school and unable to see him before late afternoon. I reflected on the way home that he never asked for a newspaper these days. Always an avid reader of current affairs, he had then 'relaxed' by completing the crossword in less than fifteen minutes. I wondered if he had lost interest in the world outside or whether he had discovered he now lacked the necessary concentration for the crossword.

Arriving back just as the coach pulled up at the gate, I waved to Minty's friend with whom she had spent the previous evening.

"Say thanks to Mum and Dad," I called. "I'll phone them later."

As we entered the lounge she seemed eager to tell me something. "I'll put the kettle on," she offered. "How's Dad?"

"He did very well yesterday: it was a difficult time."

"Did Nan mind I didn't go?"

"I think she understood. What was it you wanted to tell me?"

"I told Jackie what you said about weddings, and thinking of something else – different - like a holiday."

Intrigued, I wondered what substitute her friend had considered.

"No, Jackie says nothing is better than getting married, but I thought of something."

"Is it going to cost a lot of money?" I teased her.

"No money," she assured me.

She paused and then announced. "If I can't get married, I'll just be famous instead!"

Life was certainly not short of challenges these days!

"I'm going to have to think about that one Minty. Famous eh?"

In the meanwhile, we settled for poached eggs on toast. Caviar was for *another* day!

In the weeks that led up to Christmas, Bob seemed to reach a plateau, and the lack of any further progress had an increasingly adverse effect on his outlook.

"I'm getting nowhere, and the days are eternal," he complained.

"You have done so much so fast," his consultant countered. "Quite honestly when you came here in September, I didn't think you'd sit on the edge of the bed, and yet you have already walked across the ward."

"That was three weeks ago, and since then, nothing. If the next spurt is not yet, I might as well be at home and do my exercises there."

"Give it a couple more weeks and we'll review the situation. You've done amazingly well." And followed by his junior staff, he left Bob to go to the next patient.

All the way home I pondered the implications of Bob leaving hospital, for that surely was the next step. In some ways it would be less demanding than the thirty-mile round trip to visit in afternoons or evenings, and if he personally were more content, the limbs might respond accordingly. Still that left arm was lifeless, though he was able to drag his left leg sufficiently behind his right to walk with only one stick now.

I talked with Minty over supper and explained that Dad was getting restless to leave hospital. Without contemplating the if, how,

or when, she stated simply, "So I'll be his nurse while you're at school, and go off duty when you come home."
She could, without any difficulty, make tea, coffee and sandwiches. She could also use the phone as long as I wrote my number boldly on a card and I was only ever five minutes away in an emergency.

"Minty you're a pet, but what about all the lovely things you do at the Centre at Christmas time?" And then I remembered that all her special events were after my term ended. It might just work. Bob could have spells at home and hospital according to his need. "I'll talk to the doctor tomorrow."

When I arrived next day, his doctor was involved in conversation with two of Bob's colleagues from the Science Department of the school where he taught.

"I don't see why not," he was saying. "I think it might be a jolly good idea - yes I'm sure he would enjoy that."
They told me their plans for a Science Department dinner just before the end of term.

"We want Bob to come - two of us will collect him with the wheelchair. We've chosen a good pub not far from here. The only problem is the restaurant part is upstairs, but don't you worry, we'll manage."
I smiled at the two of them - they were both tall, broad shouldered rugby players.

"He'll probably enjoy that most of all," I said. "Coming down might be interesting though, after a few glasses!"
They laughed good naturedly, and went off to tell Bob of their scheme. They had given him an aim, and he could talk of little else.

"No spouses coming," Andy explained. "As soon as you have a crowd in which half the people don't know each other, you lose the easy atmosphere, and everything's formal and polite."

I knew that wasn't the only reason. They wanted to show him they were mates, and that if finally he had to go back to teaching in a wheelchair, then they would be there to make it easier. Each day I was given instructions about what to bring in prior to the night...which suit, which tie...some cash so that he could stand his round.

But as the date approached, other symptoms manifested themselves and the uncertainty deepened. His left leg became increasingly stiff and swollen, and walking was more painful. He wasn't capable of the same effort at the physiotherapy sessions, and the new therapist, who had not witnessed the phenomenal progress of the autumn, was less encouraging than Liz had been. I knew the latter's move to Devon would have an impact on him, but it was unfortunate her departure coincided with this latest setback.

"Do you feel up to the evening out?" I asked. "They'll understand if you want to change your mind."

"I'll go." Totally unaware of their motive for taking him, he added, "but I'll tell John that you'll have to come as well."

Next day, we went to collect him for the weekend. Minty held the car door, whilst I positioned the chair by the passenger seat. I relieved him of the bag of pyjamas and books he had carried down in his lap, and carelessly put them on the bonnet, whilst transferring him to the car, and the wheelchair to the boot. It was Minty who, a half-hour later, reminded me I hadn't put the bag inside. Of course, it was no longer there, and wearily I turned the car, driving slowly in the hope of seeing the bag on the roadside. We got all the way back to the parking bay at the hospital and still no sight of it. I asked at the Lost Property Department, and yes, they had a bag handed in by the driver of the car who ran over it. The spines of the books were broken, and the pages muddy, but worst of all Bob had put his reading glasses in with them. They were shattered.

Desperate and frustrated that I could have been so stupid, I pondered how to get him to the optician for their replacement, when unaccountably he said, "It doesn't matter -my others will do."

But his other pair was for distance. So it wasn't only newspapers he had stopped reading; the books he took in each week were a front. Clearly he wasn't reading at all. Yet strangely, he appeared unconcerned. Nothing made sense.

I returned him to the ward on Monday as usual, but on Tuesday our friend was there before me, and was looking a little worried. Bob was rubbing his eyes, as if from strain.

"He says the glasses are causing it," he told me, and I explained about the accident I had had.

"I've still got the pieces in my bag - do you think a replacement pair could be made without Bob having to make the journey? Because of the coincidence it did not occur to me that the two factors were not cause and effect.

"Give them to me," Jeff said kindly, "I'll take them now. You stay with him. I'll go to the optician near home."
Somehow he prevailed upon the optician to make them up while he waited, and that evening he drove me back to the hospital.

Bob wasn't well enough and made the decision himself not to go to the dinner, and I promised we would have a celebration instead when he came home, in an effort to give him another target to look forward to. But what if the medics thought otherwise: I knew his ward was to be closed for the holiday period, but they may transfer him to an alternative one. If that were indeed the case, I didn't look forward to being the one to tell.

CHAPTER TWENTY TWO

In the event Bob was discharged from the hospital in time for Christmas, and leaving Minty behind to add the final touches to the party fare we had prepared the night before, I rushed from school to collect him. Closest friends and neighbours would be there to welcome him. As I gathered his belongings, I studiously ignored my observation that all was not well. He had returned from the physiotherapy unit the previous day with a blinding headache and lack of vision. This was to be dismissed by a nurse as 'probably fear of leaving the hospital'.

"It's a common feeling," was her explanation. "They all want to go home, and then when it comes to it they are scared."
I despised the lack of care, knowledge and sensibility that caused her to reflect so. She had had months to get to know him better than that, and to become cognisant of his illness.

"I thought this day would never come," he sighed with relief as between us we awkwardly installed him in the wheelchair, and I was glad that he looked less bluish-grey than yesterday.

"Headache gone?" I asked.

"It's not so bad. Nothing matters now that I'm going home," and then, "Your place or mine?" he joked.
The spirit of the man was indomitable, and I loved him. How could the nurse have lumped him in a mere 'they'. He was like no-one else I knew.

"Mine - but it will cost you. I'm cheaper by the week mind!"

And so we bandied words all the way home, and to myself I vowed I would find somewhere for him other than this hospital, should the deterioration of the past two days continue. Whatever 'National Health' excuses there were for the appalling standards of care and hygiene in the ward we had just left, he would not return.

I pulled into the drive, thrilled by the number of cars parked along the pavement. Two friends appeared with Minty at the doorway and I smiled my thanks to Jeff who had made and positioned a ramp for Bob. At the sight of them he broke-down for the first time, and tears flowed freely as they moved forward to assist him.

"Buggered if you will," he choked, but he allowed me to support him from behind, as with immense difficulty he levered himself into a standing position. He slithered one foot slightly ahead of the other providing me with the opportunity to push my right foot under his left, thus giving it the necessary height to negotiate the sill. There was a great cheer as he got inside the door, and from somewhere - and most surreptitiously - the wheelchair was right behind his backside again, and he slumped into it.

"What's your handicap these days?" he asked a golfing friend. You'd better book in a few practice rounds before the spring comes!"

Thus he rose to the occasion, clearly delighted. And never once leaving his side was Minty, holding his limp, lifeless left hand in hers as he made a short but jovial speech, the effort of which fatigued him. He remembered Ken's birthday was on St David's Day and challenged him to a jog around the block when March 1st arrived. Everyone had been forewarned of the need for rest, and two hours was the limit he could be expected to keep going. The party must have been the shortest on record, but quite the most heart-warming.

By Christmas Eve however it became evident that he was not going to enjoy the festivity we had planned; he had no interest in food, treats or visitors. Sitting in the wheelchair and supported by three pillows, he was content to let Minty open his gifts, valuing only our presence. He placed his 'good' hand on our daughter-in-law's tummy, several times. "That's my grandson," he whispered feebly.

With the advent of the New Year, I needed no expert to tell me what was going to happen. Weight was falling away; hospitals could do no more, so we may as well be close together in whatever time we had left. He could now do nothing for himself. Nurses came four times each day to inject him, and longstanding friends - and acquaintances we hardly knew - overwhelmed us with their generous offers of help.

Minty stayed home and slept long each afternoon, for it was she who, hearing me respond to the two hourly ringing of the alarm through the night, would help me to lift and turn him as he slept. Her love was infinite, and she neither complained nor wearied of the situation, and with a wisdom I shall never understand, *she* prepared *me* for the inevitable, with a degree of perception I found almost impossible to believe.

Our doctor called whenever he was in the area, and many times when he had no other need to be. When deep snow prevented driving the car, he came on foot. He recognised the rapidly dwindling stamina, and when eventually incontinence set in, he insisted that hospital care be reconsidered. I refused to contemplate a return to the hospital we had so recently left, and pleaded for re-admission to the London Hospital, but were Bob to have occupied a bed there, then someone else might have been refused an emergency operation such as he had endured in July. That could not be and I resolved to find a way to cope at home.

But resolve is sometimes not enough. One particular practical and compassionate district nurse told me of a specialist in terminal disease, who might be persuaded to see Bob even though we were outside his area. I would need our own doctor's help, which of course was forthcoming, and the two of them came to the bungalow together.

The briefest of examinations was enough for the specialist to suggest that Bob should enter 'his' hospice in a town thirty miles away. We talked about the arrangements, and the possibility of Minty and me going to stay there too.

"You can if there is a room available," he conceded hesitantly, "but I can't promise."

I think he feared that unless he could guarantee our united admission, then we might reconsider, so he changed the subject to Minty's drawings that she was selling to friends at ten pence a time to raise money for the Kielder Centre.

"And how much is this masterpiece, young lady?" the specialist asked her.

There was a long pause before Minty lifted her eyes to meet his. "How much is it for us all to go to your hospital?" was her reply.

We all three entered St Helena Hospice a few days later. I told Bob a lie and said we were going to a clinic where he could be treated by the best possible specialists. I do not know how much he realised for deep drowsiness protected him from anything like the intellectual exercise of which he would normally have been capable. Certainly if he had even moments of suspicion, sleep quickly stole them away from him, and he would wake, momentarily refreshed and cheerfully optimistic.

The nurses all wore white, and he appeared to be under the impression we were in a Canadian hospital. Everything was so beautifully and restfully arranged, and it was ironic that all through the autumn when he had been in such dreary surroundings, he had the faculties to notice things and now that everything was perfect, he was barely aware. And yet he picked up the atmosphere, and many times asked, "How did you find this place? I feel so content here. So clean." And then he would sleep again.

For just three mornings he was able to appreciate the delight of a bath. The very latest in medical equipment levered him gently into the waiting soapsuds though he needed two nurses to support him, and before he could be towelled, he was beginning to doze again.

Minty and I shared a room upstairs, where a very thoughtful member of staff had put a television for her to enjoy whilst I was with Bob. Our room overlooked his, with its patio doors onto a veranda and lakeside, and many times throughout the night I watched nurses turning and medicating him. We were onlookers now, and could do no more for him than to be there when he awoke for a moment or two. Here in the place that concerned itself with death, it seemed that those involved had discovered the only way to live. My girl was drawn to their community to such a degree that she frequently disappeared to visit elderly patients who had entered the hospice at an earlier stage of their illness than Bob. They knew what was happening to them, and gently and graciously, accepted the passing of their last weeks and months. I suspect she listened to some of the counselling team, for it was she who told me that 'Dad wouldn't need his body much longer because it was causing him pain, like shoes that were too tight. Soon he would leave it and feel better without it.'

That simple faith she imbibed at the hospice has stayed with her ever since. Often she will appear at breakfast saying, "I had a word with Dad last night. He wants us to be brave and happy." I do not presume to comment on the credibility of her words, or question whether it is imagination, or a child's ability to 'get through the eye of a needle'. Extra sensory perception? A compensatory talent afforded to those who are afflicted in other ways? I have no idea.

As the days passed, so Bob slept longer and longer; often twenty-three hours out of twenty-four. Life had gone full circle. On one occasion he slept for three days. I drove back to the bungalow for changes of clothes, fearing, as I always did, that when I returned, he would have slipped into a coma, and was therefore more than a little surprised, when I returned, to find him sitting up in the armchair. He greeted me warmly though with gestures that were very feeble, obviously thinking I had only popped out for a few minutes, for he began, "As I was telling you Helen..." and then he forgot what it was he thought he had been telling me. So sitting on the footstool by his

236

side, I told *him* something I had wanted to say for weeks whilst he had slept.

I longed to purge myself of the guilt of leaving someone who, though we could not have known it then, had less than three years to live. Who would have guessed that growing surreptitiously in that lively and active mind, was a malignant tumour? I leaned my head gently on his shoulder and begged his forgiveness. By what means I did not understand, and though he was so very weak, we had, in the next few minutes, the most wonderfully normal conversation.

"Don't say that Helen." He lightly pressed his fingers on mine. "It's the best thing that could have happened. My only regret is that you didn't leave years before when it all started going wrong. Look at the marvellous times we've had since...All these days when we've been together...really together with time to talk...talk about now, not the past, or how we'll cope with the future, but the 'now' of each day...Do you remember our visits by the Seine... I'm so glad you're my wife."

"In *spite* of everything?"

"*Because* of everything. It's been good being married to you. But I tell you what...the second time round was best!"

Feeling suddenly exhausted, and yet utterly, utterly content, I joined him in sleep until two nurses came and lifted him back to bed.

"You look happier," one of them said quietly. "You talked?"

I nodded, for no words would come. Bob did not wake again.

That was to be our last conversation, for he died a few days later. He was only fifty-one and it all seemed so horribly unfair. I prayed I would never again be called upon to watch a member of my family suffer in such a cruel way. To witness daily the disintegration of the body was something so dreadful that the memory of it remains an obstacle to sleep, accompanies me as surely does my shadow and is a haunting recurrent nightmare.

At his funeral, my flowers were not a wreath, but a bouquet of white roses; the white roses he planned to give me 'for all the world to see.'

For a long time afterwards, and installed at Three Farthings, the exercising of our dog down the lane provided me with the rational reason I needed for being there; a disguise for the emotional reality of searching for a lost partner who had begun every day by jogging along this very road. I could tread his footsteps; could whisper to him whilst to anyone else who found sleep elusive, my demeanour would suggest nothing more than an awareness of the early morning chill.

Here in the solitude of the dawn I could give vent to the tears that must stay imprisoned throughout the daytime requirement of appearing to be in control, listening to trivial matters and irritating pettiness, whilst I yearned for understanding of *my* grief. Such a desperate feeling of being abandoned, and the fear of coping with the rest of life alone. And then without even looking to make sure I was alone, I'd cry out, "Where have you gone? Why did you have to leave us?"

I was surely going mad; searching for the unobtainable. And then I would return to wake Minty, the only person to whom madness, if it were ever to be diagnosed, would make not the slightest difference to her love for me.

We go often to the tiny Norman church in our village, and walk to the highest point of the churchyard where Bob is buried. It seems stupid to say that I chose that spot rather than one lower down beside the pathway, because he loved the view from there. We go to be near to him for a while because this is the last place we left him. Minty understands. We arrange the flowers we have brought, and I have to read the memorial stone to convince myself he has really gone.

The stonemason asked if, after the 'In Loving Memory' bit, I'd like a personal inscription of any kind. I declined because the only one I wanted would have appeared in bad taste, and been totally misunderstood by others who read it. Bob would have chided me for conforming again, for what did it matter so long as he and I understood? The only inscription I would have chosen was the one that captured the memory for all time of that wonderful 'strawberry and cream day' at Penshurst, so succinctly recorded by the old lady. "Ee, yer can tell they're not married, can't yer?"

Minty chats away to Bob, not with any reverence, but naturally, as if she can feel him there. I don't intrude on this private but open conversation that I suppose any eavesdropper would dismiss as that of a simple mind. But I wonder. Except ye become as a little child..... We both say goodbye; I with longing and regret, and she with an apparent belief that he is as near as in the days when we were forever tripping over his wellies in the kitchen.

How trivial the irritations that drove us apart now seem; how minuscule compared to the sheer luxury of having a lifetime companion; someone with whom to grow old and share the precious years that are left. How void and meaningless is a life alone. It is not simply a matter of a human being to fill the gap, for only the partner who is also parent to the offspring fits into the family unit as the grain is natural to the wood. Because we are of each other, so both hurt and happiness are more intense; meaningful in a way they could never be to a new partner.

As we leave the churchyard to return to the house he built for us, Minty asks, "When I die, will I be planted with you and Dad in that little garden?" Only she could express a burial in such terms, with all that the concept suggests. From so many years first hand experience, I know her to be that most special person Doc Cruickshank promised so long ago on a winter's night in Canada, to two people who could only think that their world had fallen apart.

The idea of us all blooming again lightens our spirit, and I squeeze her hand. "One day Minty." And silently I add, "but not yet; please God not yet."